red-flannel hash and shoo-fly pie

American Regional Foods and Festivals

Also by Lila Perl

WHAT COOKS IN SUBURBIA

THE DELIGHTS OF APPLE COOKERY

red-flannel hash

and shoo-fly pie

American Regional Foods and Festivals

LILA PERL

Illustrated by Eric Carle

THE WORLD PUBLISHING COMPANY

CLEVELAND AND NEW YORK

Published by The World Publishing Company
2231 West 110th Street, Cleveland 2, Ohio
Published simultaneously in Canada by
Nelson, Foster & Scott Ltd.
Library of Congress Catalog Card Number: 65-13417
FIRST EDITION
M W P
Designed by Jack Jaget

CONTENTS

THE SOUTH

THE MIDWEST AND THE GREAT PLAINS

introduction

THIS BOOK tells the story of what Americans eat, and why. To tell this story, it reaches back four hundred years into the history of the United States and ranges the breadth of that land from Maine to Hawaii.

The growth of the United States was by regions, distinct and separate areas of development isolated from one another by factors of both space and time. Within these areas a rich ferment of local and domestic life bubbled for many years.

In each region the people of the Old World, set down in the New World, produced styles of architecture, habits of dress, methods of work, modes of relaxation, and patterns of cookery that were unique. The Dutch burghers in New Amsterdam, the French aristocrats in Louisiana, the Scandinavian farmers in the Midwest—all adapted their habits, skills, and traditions to the land and its resources.

Nor can we ignore the basic contribution of the first Americans, the Indians, who were a guiding force, often silent, often understandably hostile, but without whom survival in the wilderness-world of three and four centuries ago might not have been achieved.

Just as no history book can give us a rounded picture of a people's past without telling us something about their food products and eating habits, it is impossible to tell the story of American cookery without telling something of American history. It is even more unthinkable, in discussing a nation's cuisine, to omit its geography. Nor can the holidays and festivals, any more than the cooking methods and table etiquette of a people, be left out of such a discussion.

Many people argue that America's eating habits are no longer regional but have become national. The invention of the Mason jar and the tin can, of mechanical refrigeration, flash food freezing, and jet aircraft has not only eliminated regional boundary lines but has nearly done away with climate variations and with the seasons themselves.

Thus a frozen Pennsylvania Dutch shoo-fly pie can be purchased in a California supermarket, and Alaskan king crab is available in a New Jersey food emporium. The Alaskan Eskimo eats canned peaches for dessert instead of a lump of blubber-rich *muktuk,* and the Hawaiian forsakes his native poi-and-coconut pudding for a packaged angel-cake mix that has been manufactured in Minneapolis. What, you may then ask, has become of American regional cookery?

The answer is that American regional cookery has most certainly *not* vanished. It has only expanded. It has left its root soil to reach across the continent and even across an ocean. As a result we may not always find regional dishes where we expect to find them. Some may be difficult to recognize at first; others may well be on their way to disappearing forever. Hawaiian poi and Alaskan musk ox, for example, are not likely to travel far from home. The New England housewife's salt-rising bread, prepared by a long and complicated all-day process, then baked all night in a brick fireplace oven, is most probably a thing of the past.

It is a challenge to search out the origins of the foods we eat, and in so doing to keep alive our rich and vibrant heritage. It is also rewarding to prepare regional dishes from America's colorful past. To this end, simple but authentic recipes appear at the close of each regional chapter. The recipes have been carefully tested and especially chosen with an eye to availability of ingredients and ease of preparation for less experienced cooks and even for non-cooks. Among these fifteen recipes you will find corn oysters and Indian pudding from New England, hush puppies and pecan pie from the deep South, chili con carne from the Mexican-influenced Southwest, and many more, including recipes from Alaska and Hawaii. They are all yours to make, to taste, and to enjoy. Together they tell a wonderful story—the story of America.

red-flannel hash and shoo-fly pie

American Regional Foods and Festivals

NEW ENGLAND

Maine
New Hampshire
Vermont
Massachusetts
Rhode Island
Connecticut

INDIAN PUDDING, red-flannel hash, baked beans with brown bread; codfish cakes and johnnycake; apple pandowdy and pumpkin pie. How unmistakably all of these foods say New England to us!

Yet these were not always the native dishes of New England. Through the long silent centuries before the earliest European explorers touched its shores, before the ancestors of the Indian drifted across the continent from west to east, this land was slowly being shaped by giant forces of nature.

The red men who came at last to dwell in what is now the northeast corner of the United States found a country of ancient mountains, worn smooth and low by great glaciers. They found swift foaming streams and waterfalls, numerous valleys hemmed in by boulder-studded hills, and great forested slopes of sugar maple, oak, elm, beech, and majestic white pine that grew 200 feet high.

They found a rugged seacoast so full of inlets, bays, and coves as to appear carved by some prehistoric jigsaw. Rivers flowed from the inland mountains to the sea, and there were many ponds and lakes. On the sandy ocean beaches the red men found bushes of spicy purple beach plums, and the low marshy country nearby, known as bogland, was dotted with small ruby cranberries.

About 1000 A.D. when the Norsemen, under Leif Ericson, came in their dragon-headed ships to the shores of North America, they named it Vinland, after the thick clusters of wild grapes they found along the coast.

We do not know exactly where these bold Scandinavian sailors put ashore, but evidence points to the southern coast of Massachusetts' Cape Cod or to the vicinity of Rhode Island. Had Leif Ericson or his countrymen (who continued to make visits to North America until about 1347) ever succeeded in establishing a permanent colony on these shores, this chapter might very well have been titled Vinland instead of New England, and the foods and cookery of the region would be remarkably different from what they are today.

But the Norsemen failed, or perhaps they were not really interested in planting a settlement in a fierce new land so far from home. In any event their voyages to the cape that jutted like a beckoning arm into the sea ceased. Nearly three hundred years were to pass before voyagers from the Old World were to found their first permanent settlement.

THE FOODS OF THE NEW ENGLAND INDIANS

We often wonder why the Pilgrims at Plymouth (and before them the settlers at Jamestown) suffered such agonies of starvation in a land where the Indian had managed to feed himself successfully for hundreds of years.

Indeed, the woods of New England were bursting with game—elk, moose, deer, bear, hordes of smaller edible animals, and wild turkeys reputed to have stood 3 feet tall and to have weighed 30 to 40 pounds. In season, ducks, geese, and other waterfowl flapped thickly overhead. Pheasants and partridges were plentiful, and passenger pigeons so numerous that their massed flights were said to have darkened the sky at midday.

The Indians of the New England area, who were members of the great Algonquian family, built no sea-going vessels, probably because they never felt the need to. Fish abounded in the lakes and rivers. Each spring the shad, a full-bodied fish of the herring family, left its ocean home and swarmed up the Connecticut and other New England rivers to lay its eggs. The Indian's catch of these spawning fish was so heavy that he often placed a whole shad in each hillock of seed to fertilize his maize patches, a practice he later taught to the Pilgrim settlers.

Along the ocean shore, shellfish, and especially the quahog, a hard-shell clam, were to be had for the digging. The quahog, in fact, was a principal means of survival for the Pilgrims at Plymouth during the spring and summer of 1621 while they waited for the first crops to mature.

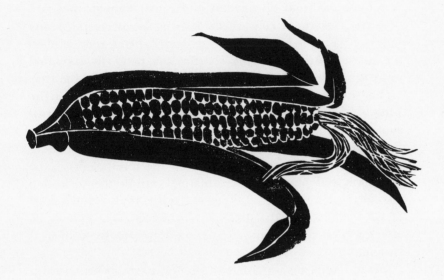

But the true staple of Indian life, in other parts of the country as well as in New England, was maize, or "Indian corn," as the startled Europeans called it. For this was a grain that was neither sown nor reaped in the fashion of European grains such as wheat, oats, rye, or barley.

The simple method by which corn could be planted and grown was a life-giving advantage to the Indians who, we must remember, were still a Stone Age people at the time of Columbus. They knew almost nothing of metals and their uses and had never dreamed of such a thing as an iron rake or hoe. Neither had the Indian discovered the wheel and its uses—and as to horses, these animals had been nonexistent in America since prehistoric times when the Indian's ancestors had hunted them for food.

Plowing a field for planting with such primitive wood or bone implements as the Indian had was an almost impossible task in the rocky, stumpy soil of New England. To plant corn, however, it was not necessary to plow. The earth could simply be piled up into long rows, or hills, and the seed dropped in.

Clearing heavily treed areas for planting offered a problem that the Indians met in one of two ways. One method was to smear mud all around and up and down the bark of a tree, leaving a ring of dry bark at about the swinging height of a stone-headed ax. The dry ring of bark was then set ablaze until thoroughly charred. By patiently chopping away at the charred portion, the Indians soon felled the tree.

The other, slower method was that of girdling, or stripping the bark from a tree so that although it remained standing for a time it would soon die, permitting the sun to shine through its leaflessness to the ground. The corn could then be planted in sunny patches on the forest floor.

Squash and pumpkin were planted amidst the corn, and also beans. Their vines climbed the tall corn, making a kind of *sukquttahash* on the stalk. (This Indian dish, a combination of cooked corn and beans, was later to be known as succotash.)

Corn, like beans, squash, and pumpkin, could be dried for winter use, an important consideration in the New England climate with its short growing season and long snowy winters. The dried corn kernels, which had been stripped from the cob, were either cooked whole as hominy, or were pounded into meal in a mortar, a huge, deep bowl-shaped vessel usually made of a hollowed-out tree trunk. The pestle, or pounder, was a club of heavy wood.

This tedious and almost never-ending task fell to the women of the tribe, for corn meal gave the Indians their bread. Mixed with a little water, it could be patted into flat cakes to be baked in the hot ashes of the fire. More often it was cooked with water in a "kettle" of birch bark, wood, or simple pottery over an open fire, to make a porridge called samp, or what we would probably call corn-meal mush.

The Indians of the northeastern woodlands were luckier

than most, for they had discovered a delicious sweetener to add to their diet. This was the sap of the sugar maple which they had learned to extract by tapping. Just how this discovery came about is unknown, but legend has it that an Indian squaw who was about to cook a potful of moose meat for her brave noticed "water" dripping from a nearby tree. Since she was busily working on a pair of moccasins at the time, she decided to forgo the long walk to the spring and filled the pot of meat chunks with "tree water" instead. The "tree water," or sap, soon cooked to a thick golden sirup, and as she worked on unaware the pot bubbled merrily and the sirup crystallized into a richly flavored caramel-colored sugar. Her warrior husband, it is said, pronounced the mess delicious. In any event she had discovered both maple sirup and maple sugar.

Nut oils, fish oils, and bear grease also contributed flavoring to Indian foods, and even more important, fat. For the Indian liked a thick layer of grease on his food whenever he could get it. It was for this reason that he added the sunflower to the short list of foods that he cultivated, eating the seeds whole, or crushing them for the oil they provided. Nuts, including walnuts, hickories, butternuts, and chestnuts; wild fruits such as plums, crabapples, and grapes; and dozens of varieties of wild berries, among them blueberries and blackberries, gooseberries, cranberries, and raspberries, helped to round out the food supply of the New England tribes.

This then was the food story of the northeastern woodland Indian on the eve of the Pilgrim landing at Plymouth Rock. We must not, however, be led into believing that the cooking pot brimming with *sukquttahash,* the roasting venison haunch, the samp porridge coated with bear grease, came easy to the New England Indian. The job of obtaining and storing food was one that occupied him every single day of his life.

Most Indian communities were small because, despite his skills, the Indian's primitive hunting and agricultural methods could produce just so much food. There were fewer than one million Indians living in all of North America at the time of Columbus (as against 190,000,000 people in the United States alone today), and it is estimated that the average Indian village seldom consisted of more than 150 people. As a village became too large a group of people had to split off and leave, going in search of new hunting and planting grounds on which to settle.

Two things accounted, therefore, for the Indian's success at gathering an adequate food supply in a land where starvation was to claim the lives of so many from that much more advanced civilization across the sea. One was the Indian's comparatively small numbers in a very large country; the other was his perfect adaptation, through his experience and his skills, to the land and its climate.

The Pilgrims settling on the Massachusetts coast, building their snug compact houses and planting their patches of Indian corn and English garden vegetables, seem so right an image to us that it is hard to realize that their landing on that wintry, rocky shore in December of 1620 was something of an accident. Their original plan had been to settle in Virginia, several hundred miles to the south.

THE PILGRIM SETTLERS ARRIVE

We are not absolutely certain whether this change in plans was due to a navigational error on the part of the *Mayflower*'s captain or to a decision, made at sea by his passengers, to stay free of land belonging to the London Company (as did the Virginia territory). Or perhaps the landing in New England was due to the fury of the Atlantic storms and tides that seemed to push the *Mayflower* ever northward. In any case the Pilgrims found themselves on an inhospitable shore in December, a time of year that was neither pleasant nor fruitful.

To add to this difficulty the travelers had not brought an adequate food supply. Quarters aboard the *Mayflower,* which was unbelievably small for the 102 passengers it carried, were cramped, and the main concern had been for food to eat on shipboard during the long weeks at sea—biscuits (crackers), cheese, butter, bacon, salted fish, root vegetables, and dried fruits. Much of this food spoiled during the long damp journey, and most of it was eaten, spoiled or not, by the time land was sighted.

The newcomers arrived with their memories, some bags of seeds with which to sow barley, wheat, and oats, peas and other garden vegetables, a few iron cooking vessels, and quite empty stomachs. They were almost wholly dependent on the wildlife of the country for meat, but to their misfortune they were weak in hunting skills. For most of the Pilgrim band were townspeople, mainly artisans or small tradesmen; some were farmers. They were as unprepared for life in the American wilderness as is the American city dweller of today for life in the jungles of New Guinea.

Yet from these desolate beginnings the New England settlers produced a variety of foods both old and new, new cooking patterns, new dishes, and a regional cuisine that was indelibly stamped with the English way of life.

FROM TISQUANTUM TO THE FIRST THANKSGIVING

Several Indian names are linked with those of the first settlers in Massachusetts (which itself takes its name from that of an Algonquian Indian tribe). But it was the Indian Tisquantum, often spoken of as Squanto, who was probably most responsible for the Pilgrims' survival, such as it was, during the winter of 1620–21.

For Tisquantum was, of all things, an English-speaking Indian who with several others of his tribe had been taken to England some fifteen years earlier and later returned to America. How startling and pleasant that first experience of simple communication must have been for the low-spirited settlers. Despite the help of Tisquantum and his English-speaking tribal brother Samoset, only 50 of the 102 passengers who had landed from the *Mayflower* lived to see the New England spring.

During the first winter some of the settlers lived in rude huts or lean-tos of poles with thatched roofs. Others lived on board the *Mayflower*. Their food consisted of the remains of the meager rations they had brought with them from England, much partially rotted corn left from the previous Indian harvest, and what game the Indians provided or taught them how to kill for themselves.

With the coming of spring the settlers planted, under Indian guidance and in Indian fashion, corn, squash, pumpkins, and beans, as well as the seeds of oats, wheat, barley, and peas that they had brought with them from England. But the harvest was not yet at hand and the spring and early summer were a difficult time—wild berries and fruits not yet ripe, the corn just sprouting green, and the English wheat withering strangely in the rich new soil. It was during this time that the quahog and other shellfish, which Tisquantum had taught the settlers to dig for along the sandy shore, kept them alive and hopeful.

If we think about the great outdoor harvest feast of 1621, which is said to have lasted an entire week, we soon realize that we are in error to celebrate Thanksgiving late in November as we do now. For November is a bleak time in New England, the cold already damp and penetrating near the coast, and most of the harvest long past gathering. It is more likely that the golden days of early October saw the first Thanksgiving to which scores of Indians, led by the chief Massasoit, came bringing much venison and other game.

Wild duck, bear meat, and shellfish were also served, but it was the wild turkey, native to New England woodlands, that was the glory of the feast. So plentiful were these huge birds of the forest that even one hundred years later they were selling for as little as one and half pence a pound in western Massachusetts, and it was not until the middle of the nineteenth century that the last of the wild turkeys had been shot in New England.

It is doubtful that wild turkey—dark-meated, muscular, and probably more than a little tough—was much like the plump, tender domesticated birds we know today. The forty-pounders of colonial times were too large for any roasting pan and sometimes so covered with ticks that they had to be skinned and then encased in clay, Indian fashion, to preserve their flavor and juices while being slowly spit-roasted over the open fire.

Succotash prepared with sun-dried corn kernels and small dried pea beans, seasoned with bear fat; chunks of stewed pumpkin and squash; wild berries and fruits; and Indian meal sweetened with shaved maple sugar or wild honey—all of these were served at the first Thanksgiving.

Cranberries, originally named crane berries by the Pilgrims because their white blossom and stem resembled the head and the neck of a crane, have become a Thanksgiving tradition. They may not have been present, however, at that first feast, since they require so much sweetening in their preparation. Cane sugar was not to appear in New England for many years, and maple sugar, in the early days of settlement, was reserved for cooking with less tart foods such as pumpkin, squash, and corn meal.

Potatoes were most certainly absent from the first Thanksgiving. The white potato, native to South America and especially Peru, had never been grown in North America and was not to be introduced for cultivation in New England until 1719, nearly one hundred years after the first Thanksgiving. Oddly enough it was to reach North America by way of Europe. Brought back to Spain from South America by the Spanish explorers, the white potato had been introduced in England by Sir Walter Raleigh and then into Ireland where it became a staple, or basic, food. For this reason the white potato is also called the Irish potato.

The sweet potato, native to warmer climates, did not grow north of the eastern shore of Maryland, and its appearance on the Thanksgiving menu began in the South, most probably in the Virginia colony.

Nor did delectable mouth-watering holiday pies—mince, pumpkin, apple—make an appearance at the Pilgrim festivities in 1621. For the settlers had little or no wheat flour, or even rye flour, for the pie crusts. They did not have spices, or suet (beef or mutton fat), or raisins for mincemeat, and they had none but the undersized and sour crab-apple, which grew wild across the face of North America, to use for an apple-pie filling!

The idea of celebrating a day of thanksgiving, which combined the tradition of the old English harvest festival with the celebration of the Pilgrims' deliverance in the new land, soon spread through the colonies, with each governor proclaiming a day of feasting and prayer in the autumn of the year. It was not until 1864, however, that President Lincoln declared Thanksgiving a national holiday, to be observed uniformly throughout the country on the fourth Thursday in November.

Boston, "the home of the bean and the cod," was founded in 1630 by another group of freedom-seeking Englishmen, the Puritans. It was from this hub of the Massachusetts Bay Colony that many New England food traditions sprang, and notable among these was Saturday night baked beans.

BAKED BEANS,

CODFISH CAKES, AND

CLAM CHOWDER

There were very good religious reasons for this typical Saturday night supper in the Massachusetts colony. To keep cooking to a minimum on the day before the strictly observed Puritan Sabbath, the bean pot was put to bake on a Saturday morning, or even on Friday evening, in the slow heat of the fireplace oven. Except for the addition of a little water now and then, beans needed little tending by the busy, and often servantless, New England housewife. By suppertime on Saturday evening the beans were ready, simmering richly in their juices, fragrant with the flavors of onion, salt pork, mustard, and molasses. On Sunday morning, having been kept warm in the fireplace oven, the beans were eaten again for breakfast.

Tomato sauce, so often cooked with baked beans today, is not traditional with New England baked beans. The tomato, which originated in South and Central America, was not grown in the United States until after 1800, and even then was generally thought to be poisonous.

Within New England itself there were, and still are, differences of opinion as to how baked beans should be prepared. Bostonians use pea beans, while people in New Hampshire and Vermont prefer "yellow eyes" or "soldier beans," so called because the brown marking on the bean resembles the silhouette of an armed soldier. Vermonters will not hear of any sweetener but maple sugar for their beans, while down in coastal Boston molasses brought on ships from the West Indies in early colonial times is still the favorite.

As the settlements grew and prospered, other foods were added to the Saturday night baked-bean supper. Dark, moist brown bread, made with cornmeal, flour, molasses, buttermilk, and raisins, originated as a steamed pudding and is still baked by steaming in covered cylindrical molds, or in coffee cans. In New England, especially in Boston, brown bread is almost inseparable from baked beans. It is delicious served warm, and the slices, of course, are always round. Coleslaw and pickles are traditional with baked beans and brown bread, and so is tart-sweet applesauce. As early as 1629 the colonists had started apple orchards in New England, importing both seeds and propagating wood from England.

Indian pudding was a favorite Saturday night dessert, sharing the fireplace oven with the beans in the last hours of baking. Richer than plain yellow Indian meal cooked with water, Indian pudding was prepared with milk, molasses, spices such as cinnamon and nutmeg, and in rare cases an egg or two. Raisins were often added and sometimes even diced apples. Served warm with cream, it was, and is, a dessert of melting goodness.

Fish and the fishing industry have always been so important to the New England coast that Massachusetts has been
called the "home of the sacred cod," and a codfish was actually inscribed in the official seal of the Massachusetts Bay
Colony.

Coming as they did from England, a country surrounded
by the sea, it is not surprising that the Pilgrims and their
Puritan neighbors were such a sea-minded people. Not long
after the Pilgrims' landing at Plymouth they repaired the
Mayflower's rowboat and began to use it for offshore fishing.
But it was the port of Boston that was to become famous as
a commercial fishing center. As game in the settled areas
was killed off, many New Englanders turned to the sea rather
than the inland frontier, combining farming in the growing
season with fishing during the winter months. The New
England forests were stocked by nature with perfect ship-
building timber including the strong, light white pines used
for the tall masts of sailing ships.

As New England's fishing boats ventured farther from
shore, they began to plumb the riches of the teeming Atlantic, bringing home huge catches of cod, haddock, halibut,
and mackerel. Some of the catch was eaten fresh, but most
had to be preserved for long keeping by salting and drying,
or by smoking. By 1650 dried salt codfish was being used in
trade with the Southern colonies and the West Indies, and
was in great demand farther off in the Catholic countries of
Spain and Portugal. From these European ports came such
luxuries as dried fruits, spices, wines, and the very salt that
was used in preserving the fish.

At home the thrifty New Englanders soon found dozens
of uses for cod, whether fresh, dried, or salted—codfish cakes
and codfish balls, the salted fish soaked twelve hours, then
shredded and combined with mashed potatoes and eggs, fried
in hot fat until brown and crusty and shaggy-coated; cod
chowder, rich with milk, hearty with diced potatoes, garnished with flavorful salt-pork cracklings; boiled cod dinner
of salt cod, onions, beets, and potatoes; and fish hash fried
up the next day, crisp-edged and omelet-like, using all of the
leftovers from a boiled fish dinner. Fish hash was a breakfast

favorite served along with oatmeal, eggs, hot bread, and maybe even a slab of fried ham. In Boston tiny hot crusty codfish balls became a Sunday morning breakfast tradition.

Cape Cod turkey was the name popularly given, in an area where game was at its scarcest, to a large whole fresh-caught codfish, baked and stuffed, surrounded with all the fixings of a grand and stylish dinner. *Kedgeree,* an East Indian dish, was introduced into New England by sailing-ship captains and made good use of dried, salt fish, usually cod, combined with hard-cooked eggs, rice (which the New Englanders were soon receiving in trade with Carolina), and parsley, in a creamy white sauce.

It was not all codfish, however, in New England. Mackerel was caught in great schools in offshore waters and either eaten fresh or preserved by salting. Haddock, smaller than cod but inhabiting the same waters, was eaten fresh or, more often, smoked.

Dried and smoked haddock is affectionately known as finnan haddie, so named for the town of Findon, Scotland, where the special smoking process originated. Finnan haddie is served flaked in a cream sauce, or it may be baked whole in milk, after first being soaked in water to remove some of the strong flavor and to soften the flesh.

Shellfish, too, was an important part of New England's
fishing bounty—lobsters from Maine's icy waters, oysters,
scallops, and both hard-shell clams and the sweet soft-shell
variety. Since shellfish did not lend itself to salting, drying,
or other preserving processes known at the time, the catch
had to be eaten fresh locally, and thus originated many of
New England's seafood specialties.

In Maine fresh-caught lobsters were often steamed in sea
water for outstanding flavor, and hot nourishing lobster
stew prepared with milk and chunks of diced lobster, seasoned with onion, was considered an ideal breakfast dish by
"down-easters," as the settlers along this farthest easterly
coast were called. Or lobster stew might be eaten as a main
dish at dinnertime with dill pickles and oyster crackers.

Lobsters were caught, as they still are today, in slatted
wooden traps called lobster pots. The traps were baited with
dead fish and lowered into deep, very cold water among the
rocks. Marker buoys helped the lobstermen to locate the
traps, which were hauled up every day or two and the catch
emptied. In the early days of lobstering, these strange but
delicious creatures were so abundant off the Maine and

Massachusetts coasts that they sold for just one penny apiece!

Clams are the basis, of course, of world-renowned New England clam chowder, made with salt pork, potatoes, onions, plenty of clams, milk, some cream perhaps, but positively *no* tomatoes. Although a later version of this soup, known as Manhattan clam chowder, does include tomatoes as well as other vegetables, New Englanders stanchly maintain that the tomato overpowers the delicate flavor of the clams.

Clams are delicious, too, in a Provincetown clam pie made of tender chopped clams enclosed in a flaky pie crust, or simply dipped in batter and fried. And what would a New England clambake be without clams—or, for that matter, a New England fish fry without shad? We shall speak later about both of these popular regional outdoor festivities.

NEW ENGLAND FIREPLACE COOKERY

Our story of Boston baked beans and New England fishing has taken us past the very early Puritan days in the Massachusetts Bay Colony. As with the Pilgrims at Plymouth, this was a time when the indoor fireplace was a brand-new luxury, built to supplant the single cooking pot suspended over the open outdoor fire, and the first one- or two-room rectangular cottage replaced the wigwam-like hut of upright logs and thatch.

The fireplace was the center of colonial home life in New England, providing cooking fuel, heat, light, and cheer for the principal, and often only, room in the house. Here the children sat on winter evenings scraping dried corn kernels from the cobs or reciting their lessons, while the mother spun or wove flax for her household linens and the father carved a new wooden trencher, butter paddle, broomstick, or other household tool.

Since the colonists had brought only a few iron implements with them from England, and native iron had not yet begun to be mined, cooking pots were suspended over the fire from a lug pole of freshly cut "green" wood. The pole

rested on ledges built into the insides of the fireplace. As
the lug pole dried from the constant heat of the fire, it became charred and weakened. If not replaced in time the
lug pole collapsed, dashing a family's entire dinner into the
fire. As soon as iron became easier to get, the green-wood lug
pole was put aside forever.

From the vital lug pole were suspended the pots of samp
porridge, the kettles of stewed meat and vegetables, and the
steamed puddings that were the stand-by foods of the Puritan
household. Like Indian women before them, Pilgrim and
Puritan women now knew the burdensome task of pounding
dried corn into meal. To make the work a little easier a
pestle, or pounding club, was tied to a sapling, a flexible
young tree. The sapling did the lifting of the pestle, leaving
the housewife to do the downward pounding into the
hollowed-out tree trunk or post that served as a mortar. So
constant and resounding was the *thump-thump-thump* of the
samp mortars that it was said sailors and fishermen far out
in the fog-bound waters of the Atlantic could hear it and be
guided to shore by its sound.

Querns, primitive hand-operated mills of giant stones set
at waist height, were also used for grinding corn. But it was
not long before the power of the swift New England water-
ways was harnessed for community grist mills where the
families of the surrounding area might bring their corn for
grinding.

Other grains such as rye, oats, and barley were soon being
grown and harvested along with the corn. Oatmeal porridge
began to rival samp porridge as a breakfast food, and rye
flour came to be mixed with corn meal for a bread known
as *"rye 'n' Injun."* But wheat, the grain the colonists craved
most, was slow to take in the too-rich soil, and bread of all-
wheat flour was a rarity in New England well into the 1700s.

The baking oven was built into the brick or stone of the
fireplace wall and here corn bread or "punkin" bread (made
with corn meal and dried, ground pumpkin) was baked.
Anadama bread was a popular *raised* corn bread, leavened
with yeast. Legend has it that the bread was accidentally
discovered by a New England fisherman whose lazy, indif-

ferent wife, Anna, always gave him corn-meal mush for
dinner. One day he became so annoyed that he began to
alter the ingredients of Anna's mush, adding molasses, salt,
some flour (rye or possibly wheat), and yeast. The result
was a light, tasty loaf.

To heat the brick or stone oven, which had a flue of its
own leading into the fireplace chimney, a fire of good hot-
burning wood such as maple was laid in the oven. When the
oven had been heated sufficiently, the ashes were raked out
and the bread set in to bake overnight in the slow steady
heat retained by the brick walls. It emerged in the morning
hot, fragrant, and crusty. In colonial times it was customary
to bake bread twice a week, and always several loaves at each
baking.

The rest of the time bread needs might be taken care of
with johnnycake, a bread shaped like a large thick pancake
and made with corn meal, water, and salt. Rhode Island
johnnycake is famous and was made with white corn meal,
although most of the corn grown in New England was of the
yellow variety. The Rhode Island settlers learned about
johnnycake from the Indians who, having no ovens, had long
been baking their "bread" of meal and water, in the shape
of flat cakes, in the hot ashes of their fires.

The origin of the name *johnnycake* is something of a
mystery and probably has nothing at all to do with the name
John. Since johnnycakes could be carried on long trips in
the saddlebags of colonial travelers or even baked along the
way, it is most likely that they were really called "journey
cakes" at first. Johnnycake was baked at home in the fireplace oven or on a griddle just in front of the fire. It did not
take nearly so long to bake as did a loaf of bread, and leftover johnnycake could be eaten split and toasted.

While breads kept fairly well and dried corn and other
vegetables were dependable staples, the keeping of meat was
a very great problem for the New England colonists—as it
had been for man throughout the ages. As wild game grew
scarce in the settled areas, more cattle, sheep, and hogs were
brought to the New World from England and other parts
of Europe. Bear, elk, venison, and even wild turkey began

to give way to beef, lamb, pork, and chicken on the New England dinner table.

With most slaughtering of large animals done in the fall of the year, the meat had to be preserved by the traditional European methods of pickling, salting, and smoking. These processes, however, required salt, pepper, and other spices—and spices were in short supply in New England as they had been in Europe since the Middle Ages.

Indeed, so in demand were peppercorns, cloves, nutmegs, ginger, cinnamon, cardamom, and other spices that the Yankee peddlers, who traveled by horse and cart through the colonies selling tinware and other household goods, were said to have sold nutmegs carved of wood and soaked in nutmeg extract in place of the real thing. Connecticut, nick-named the "Nutmeg State" is said to have originally been dubbed the "Wooden Nutmeg State" for this reason.

Stewed meats were preferred to roasted meats in the early days of fireplace cookery, since they kept well and could be reheated in the same kettle meal after meal. But for special occasions large cuts of meat were roasted on a spit in the fireplace, the spit often hand-turned by a child. Later, in-genious devices were introduced for turning cuts of meat as they roasted over the open fire. One of these was known as a clock jack, and it turned by a system of wound-up springs. Another was a treadmill connected to the spit and operated by a small terrier called a "turnspit dog." A railing enclosed the eager little dog to prevent him from gobbling up the succulent joint.

About 1700 the Dutch oven came into use. This was a metal box with one open side facing the fire. A door on the other side could be opened for basting the meat, and the box had a handle on the outside so that the roast could be given an occasional turn. The Dutch oven proved so popular that thereafter only very large roasts were cooked on a spit over the open fire.

As salt and other spices became available through trade, the New Englanders began to "corn" their beef. Corning, in this case, meant salting and spicing it, as with peppercorns (the dried berries of the pepper plant) and other spices. Corned beef is responsible for the New England boiled dinner, a regional dish so popular that it was eaten at least twice a week during the winter months when no fresh meat was to be had.

For a boiled dinner the corned beef was cooked in a great kettle of water with whatever root vegetables had been stored from the summer's harvest—potatoes, turnips, onions, cabbage, carrots, parsnips—all flavored with the spiciness and salty tang of the meat. Boiled beets were also served with the dinner, but these were cooked separately so as not to stain the foods they came into contact with.

Horseradish, mustard, and pickles were served with the meat and vegetables, and of course there would be corn bread. Indian pudding was usually the dessert. Next day the leftovers were chopped and fried all together in salt-pork drippings in a heavy skillet. They were served up as red-flannel hash, crusty, well browned, and garnished with salt pork cracklings. The inclusion of the chopped beets in the hash gave it its rosy hue, the soft color of red flannel.

There were boiled ham dinners and boiled chicken dinners too, and the boiled salt cod dinner with its second-day fish hash. Fried chicken, so popular in the American South, never held a place among traditional New England dishes.

The probable reason is that frying food takes care and watching, better suited to the Southern kitchen, well staffed with
Negro slaves. For the bustling New England housewife, who
might at best have one hired girl to help with the chores,
the boiled dinner cooked in a pot that needed little watching
was a tremendous boon.

For those thin times when neither meat nor fish was to
be had New England frugality invented such main dishes as
poor man's stew and corn oysters. Poor man's stew was really
a vegetable chowder of potatoes, onions, and other root vegetables in milk, with finely diced salt pork for flavor. Corn
oysters were fritters of corn in a batter. When fried they
spread to an uneven oyster shape and curled slightly at the
edges. No oyster had ever been near them, but they made
good eating doused with maple sirup or honey.

Corn supplied the basis for other meatless dishes too—
corn chowder, and succotash prepared with corn and pea
beans or lima beans and enriched with milk and butter. In
the growing season there were always "roasting ears," as the
green, or fresh, corn was called. Roasted in its own husk in

the fireplace embers, green corn was sweet and nut-flavored, a welcome treat.

THE PURITAN FAMILY
AT TABLE

Mealtime was a solemn occasion in the Puritan household. Both the Puritan religion and the struggle for food in the early days of settlement dictated that the rough wooden trestle table and whatever bounty it held be looked upon with reverence.

At the head of the table sat the father or the man of the family. Near him sat the older boys and the woman of the house, who also did the serving unless the family had an older daughter or a hired serving girl. The younger children, however, *stood* at table, somewhere near the foot, ate whatever they were given, and were not permitted to speak throughout the meal.

Most meals consisted of a single steaming dish often served directly from the pot or kettle in which it was cooked. Large serving dishes used for bringing food to table were generally made of pewter. Smaller dishes, however, from which most people ate, were wooden trenchers—rectangular slabs of wood with an oval hollowed out on the top side. The trencher was shared by two of the children, each eating from one end. Grownups, too, ate two to a trencher except possibly the more important elders and the head of the house. It was considered extravagant in early Puritan households to have a single trencher for each member of the family. In some households there were no wooden trenchers at all but merely shallow bowl-shaped hollows carved out of the wooden table top itself.

Wooden spoons were the only "silverware." Later the settlers carved spoons and drinking cups out of horn taken from game or slaughtered domestic animals. Pewter, a dull, soft, silvery metal composed mostly of tin with lead and some copper or other metal added, had been widely used in England. The wealthier colonial families had imported spoons, mugs, and trenchers, as well as lamps and other household articles, of this material. As early as 1640 a pewterer set up shop in Boston, and little by little pewterware replaced wooden and horn tableware for most colonial families.

Forks were almost unknown in the early days of colonial New England, nor were they in common use in England at the time. The first fork to appear in England, a vicious-looking two-pronged implement, was imported from Italy during the reign of Queen Elizabeth (1558–1603). It was little more than a fad at the English court, where soft or semiliquid foods were eaten with a spoon and all the others were taken with the fingers.

The same was true in New England. Although the first fork was said to have been brought to the colonies in 1633 for Governor John Winthrop of Massachusetts, it was not until about 1700 that forks came into general use. These were still of the two-tined variety and were used only to hold the meat in place while it was being cut. No one would have dreamed of bringing food to his mouth with a fork!

Since most early New England foods were spoon foods such as porridges, puddings, and stews, knives were not very necessary to ordinary dining. Bread, broken off in chunks from the loaf rather than sliced, was not buttered and was used chiefly for mopping up gravy or meat fat. If meat or other food did have to be cut at table, one simply unsheathed his pocket knife and used that.

With so much food taken with the fingers, mealtime, even for very well-mannered people of the day, was apt to be messy, and large linen napkins were used for wiping the fingers and face. This seems like luxury in a time of frugality, but flax was grown in the colonies quite early and the women did much spinning and weaving of linen. It was not until around 1750 that three-tined forks and table knives appeared on colonial tables, and finger eating began to be considered bad manners.

The most important object on the Puritan table was the saltcellar or salt "saler," as it was called. Just as in Europe since the Middle Ages, the large salt saler that stood in the middle of the table was the symbol that divided high rank from low rank. Noblemen and others of importance sat

"above the salt"; commoners sat "below the salt." Because of the value and scarcity of salt, most of which had to be imported from Spain, the elders sat above the salt in the Puritan household; the children and any servants sat below.

We are so accustomed to thinking of the early New England settlers as being somber and conservative in their ways that we may be shocked to learn that it was common practice in the colonies for everybody in the family, including women and children, to start the day with a mug of beer or ale. Indeed, the colonists had brought barley seed with them from England for the very purpose of malting barley with which to brew beer, and breweries had, in fact, been established and licensed in New England by 1640.

As soon as apple orchards had begun to bear sufficient fruit, apple cider too became a popular drink at breakfast time and all through the day. This was not the sweet, bland fruit-juice cider that children drink today but an alcoholic beverage that varied in strength from mild to quite strong, depending on how long it had been fermented. To distinguish it from sweet cider it was called hard cider.

Rum, which was soon being manufactured in distilleries in Rhode Island, was made from molasses imported from the West Indies. It was a special favorite with seafaring men and travelers. Being stronger than either cider or beer, it was not considered a suitable family breakfast drink.

Indian pudding is probably the most traditional of New England desserts, along with its near relative hasty pudding. Hasty pudding is simply corn meal and water cooked together, Indian fashion, to a mush and sweetened with molasses, maple sirup, or shaved maple sugar. A lump of butter added to the warm hasty pudding makes it richer and tastier.

As trade brought more foods and food delicacies to New England—raisins, spices, and wines from Europe; wheat from the Hudson River valley; molasses from the West Indies; loaf sugar and later granulated sugar from New Orleans—new desserts that were a blend of traditional English dishes and of New England's regional resources came into being.

NEW ENGLAND DESSERTS

Pumpkin pie, for example, was strictly an American invention. While the English had long been making pastry for meat pies and the American Indians had long been stewing pumpkin, it took the New England colonist to combine the English pastry and the American pumpkin and come up with something that was entirely different from either.

To the mashed stewed pumpkin the colonists added milk,

eggs, spices, and molasses. The mixture was then turned into a pastry shell and baked until the filling was firm but creamy and the pie crust crisp and golden. In preparing their pumpkin-pie filling the New Englanders were following a basic English custard recipe in the use of milk and eggs. Lacking sugar, however, they added a sweet touch of their own, molasses. Molasses for pumpkin pie was, in fact, so important in colonial days that on several occasions a New England town put off its Thanksgiving celebration a week or more while awaiting a shipment of molasses from the West Indies.

Mock cherry pie prepared with Cape Cod cranberries and imported Spanish raisins; Vermont apple pie prepared with Vermont maple sirup and apples, the fruit that had been so successfully transplanted to American soil from England— both of these were examples of regional desserts that showed how people of the Old World had adapted their cookery to the resources of the new land.

Mincemeat was a very old English recipe that most certainly did not start out to be a filling for a dessert pie. Mincemeat had been devised as a means of preserving meat by mincing, or finely chopping, cooked beef and combining it with suet, dried fruits, spices, and brandy, or possibly wine. When sweetened with molasses or sugar, however, a mincemeat of diced apples, raisins, currants, and citron spiced with cinnamon, nutmeg, and cloves made a very good pie filling. With the passage of time the amount of meat in the mincemeat was decreased, or even eliminated entirely.

Therefore while English "pye" almost always meant a meat pie baked in a small casserole with a pastry crust on top, the fruit-filled dessert pies that we know today were very much an American development. In New England, where apple, pumpkin, mince, and cranberry were regional favorites, pie was eaten several times a week all the year round. And throughout the 1800s, that era of hearty dining, pie was eaten in New England even for breakfast.

Fruit desserts bearing odd names such as blueberry grunt, apple slump, and blackberry flummery followed in the tradition of English steamed pudding, but were the true product of New England cookery. Grunts and slumps, as well as cob-

blers and pandowdies, were all pretty much the same thing
—a dessert of sweetened cooked fruit (usually apples or
berries) topped with a biscuit-like dough. The dessert was
cooked by steaming in a heavy covered pot over the fire, or
baked in the oven. It was always served warm with the cream
pitcher close at hand. Pandowdy was made with apples and
was sometimes baked like a deep-dish pie with a pastry crust
on top. When the pandowdy was almost done, the pastry
topping was chopped, or "dowdied," right into the apples.
Molasses was poured over the top and the pandowdy was
baked a little longer, then served warm with cream. It was
not beautiful to look at, but its delicious taste more than
made up for its appearance.

A flummery was just a little bit different. It was a dessert
of fruit cooked with sugar and water, thickened slightly, and
served warm with cream or soft custard. It had no cakelike
topping and was supposed to be light and airy, as its name
implied.

Cakes, as we know them today, were added late to the list
of New England desserts. The ginger cakes of colonial days
were really round, flat cookies flavored with molasses and
spiced with cinnamon, nutmeg, and ginger. They were either
hard or slightly chewy, much like the gingerbread men that
are still made today. There were also sugar cakes that were
really round, flat sugar cookies. One type of New England
sugar cooky went by the delightfully funny name of Connecticut snickerdoodles.

A very traditional New England cake was Hartford elec-
tion cake, something of a cross between a bread and a cake.
Not very rich, it was raised with yeast and contained dried
fruits and spices. This type of cake was sold at town meetings
when farmers and others drove in from the countryside to
vote in local and state elections.

Surely the most luscious cake to come out of New England
was Boston cream pie. It is so great a favorite to this day
that a packaged mix for baking a complete Boston cream pie
may be purchased in supermarkets from coast to coast. Since
Boston cream pie is really a cake, there remains something
of a mystery as to why it should be called a pie.

One guess is that it was invented by a Bostonian who was

becoming tired of New England pies and pastries. He (or perhaps it was she) baked some spongecake batter in a pie pan, then turned the cake upside down, split it into two layers, and filled the center with smooth, rich custard. The top was sprinkled with powdery confectioners' sugar. In a sense Boston cream pie was the first layer cake. Today it is often baked in a round layer-cake pan instead of a pie pan, and chocolate-loving Americans spread the top with dark chocolate frosting.

FISH FRIES, CLAMBAKES, AND SUGARIN'-OFF PARTIES

Despite its Puritan heritage of frugality and hard work, New England has a host of lively and heartwarming regional festivals among its many traditions. In the early days of colonization, neighbors got together out of necessity as well as for a touch of human companionship and a bit of cheer. House-raisings, barn-raisings, and corn-husking bees were all co-operative activities that combined work with recreation. Later, with the easing of chores and the beginnings of leisure,

there were baked-bean suppers, church "sociables," skating parties, and county fairs.

Christmas was not celebrated in the early days in New England because it was a feast day of the Church of England, against which the Pilgrims and the Puritans were in rebellion. In 1659 a law was actually passed imposing a fine on anyone found observing Christmas or even resting on that day. Although Christmas gradually came to be accepted, Thanksgiving was the important New England holiday, with its festive bounty swelling each year so that a Thanksgiving dinner of the 1800s might include oysters on the half shell or oyster stew; turkey with sausage and chestnut stuffing; an enormous array of vegetables including turnips, squash, mashed potatoes, creamed onions, and succotash; cranberry sauce, pickles, and relishes; and at least three kinds of pie!

Early spring in New England, especially inland in the "sugar bush" country of Vermont and New Hampshire, meant sugar-on-the-snow parties. Nearly every farmer owned a stand of sugar maples, and each April the trees were tapped and log buckets attached to their trunks to catch the new-running sap. At "sugarin'-off" time the buckets were emptied into huge kettles and boiled over open fires out of doors, in a clearing in the bush. As the thin whitish sap bubbled away, its water content evaporated and it became a golden maple-tasting sirup.

For a sugar-on-the-snow party family and friends trooped into the still snowy woods to drizzle the pale new sirup onto mounds of scooped-up snow. The sirup, if boiled to the proper thickness, would set in little waxy pools on the snow —a delicious confection of sweetness and frost. Fresh-raised yeast doughnuts were brought along and dunked in the warm maple sirup.

In later years the work of boiling the sap down to sirup was no longer done in the open woods, but was performed indoors in a sugarhouse built for this purpose. However, the delightful tradition of the sugar-on-the-snow party lingers on in New England in the form of the sugar supper. In Vermont especially, if a fresh fall of snow coincides with "sugarin'" time, there is almost sure to be a public sugar supper held at the schoolhouse, church, or other indoor premises. A typical sugar supper menu features baked beans (sweetened with maple sugar, of course), cottage cheese, pickles, doughnuts, pans of fresh clean snow, warm maple sirup, and lots of steaming coffee.

Fish fries were another springtime event, held each year along the river banks when the shad swam from the sea up the Connecticut and other New England rivers to spawn, or lay their eggs. The spawning shad were so numerous that they were caught in nets with no trouble at all and were fried on the spot, in salt-pork drippings, in long-handled frying pans over open fires. Fried onions and potatoes were eaten along with the shad. So popular were the fries that a street in Hartford, Connecticut, on the bank of the Connecticut River was named Fishfry Street.

Fish fries were attended by men only. Since the eating of

so much fish induced thirst, a great deal of rum punch was drunk and the men tended to become very merry with much horseplay, wrestling, and other robust games to climax the occasion. The rum "punch" was really strong rum diluted with a small amount of melting river ice, so it was not surprising that the ladies stayed away.

Before shad began to decline in size and number because of increased commercial activity and the pollution of the waters, they weighed five to six pounds apiece with some whoppers running to nine pounds. (Today's shad average three pounds.) In the spring when the shad were running, families drove in by wagon from the surrounding countryside to buy as many as a hundred shad for salting, for as little as two cents each, and Vermonters brought four-to-five-pound blocks of maple sugar to trade for fish.

Alewives, a fish similar to shad, were taken in great numbers from the New England rivers during spawning season and were usually peddled by horse and cart through the back country. Their odd name is thought to be due to their heavy-bodied appearance, which resembles that of a stout woman. Members of the herring family, both shad and alewives have a great many fine small bones. Today restaurants and markets often bone shad before cooking, but New England fish lovers insist the flavor is better if shad is fried or broiled with the bones left in—and let the eater beware!

Probably the best-loved of all New England outdoor festivities is the clambake, a beach picnic that provides the most luscious of hot vittles—clams, lobsters, potatoes, and corn, cooked by steaming in a shallow pit lined with stones. The stones are fired to white heat, a process that may take four hours or more of burning kindling wood and logs right in the pit. A layer of seaweed is then placed over the heated rocks to provide moisture for steaming the food, and then the clams and the lobsters, the ears of corn in their husks, and the potatoes in their jackets are added. A heavy canvas covers the pit. While the hungry picnickers prowl the beach or amuse themselves with songs or games, the food steams on its bed of rocks and seaweed for an hour or so, to emerge hot and succulent and to be eaten at once, salted and peppered and dripping with butter.

NEW ENGLAND FOODS AND PEOPLE TODAY

The 1800s saw many changes in New England's food production. As more foods of all kinds became available and many foods began to be produced commercially, a greater variety of dishes came to grace the family dinner table both within New England and in the country and other lands beyond its borders.

White potatoes, originally a South American vegetable, were introduced in New Hampshire about 1719 by Scotch-Irish immigrants. By 1750 they were being plentifully produced in many parts of New England, and during the 1800s they became an especially important crop in the state of Maine. They continue to be so to the present. Maine's "blueberry barrens" (vast patches of blueberry bushes) produce berries marketed both fresh and canned, and her apples and sweet corn, her poultry and lobsters, have gained national renown.

Vermont, where the cows are said to outnumber the people, is famed for its cheese as well as its maple products and apples. From earliest colonial times cheese had been made at home in New England, especially in summer when milk was plentiful and would spoil quickly if not used. Cheese making was a tedious and complicated operation involving the use of rennet, extracted from a calf's stomach, to curdle the milk, and requiring a cheese press and other special equipment. Most farms had a separate cheese house or a cheese room. About 1800, however, cheese began to be made commercially in New England, and by 1850 the industry was so well established that migrating Yankees were carrying the art of cheese making into New York, Ohio, and Wisconsin.

New Hampshire, too, produces maple sirup and maple sugar and is prominent in dairying and poultrying.

On Massachusetts' Cape Cod, the cranberry-growing industry got under way in 1840 when granulated sugar became plentiful and cheap enough to guarantee a wider use of these tart, zesty little "marsh rubies," as the cranberries were called. Although not produced in quantity commercially, beach plum jelly is another Cape Cod product and a popular homemade preserve as well. Western Massachusetts grows crisp, juicy McIntosh apples. Fishing, of course, continues to be a vital industry, with Massachusetts leading the New England states.

Tomatoes were slow to gain acceptance as a food in the United States. They were introduced about 1800 and were grown for many years as a garden rarity, most people regarding them as poisonous. By about 1850, however, "love apples" (an old-fashioned name for the tomato) came to be considered edible, and New Englanders were quick to use both the ripe and green tomatoes in a variety of pickles and relishes to spice the flavors of their baked beans, stews, and chowders. Green-tomato pickle was the thrifty New England housewife's way of using the unripe tomatoes that were still on the vine when frost threatened.

Rhode Island is famed for poultry production, for its quahog clams and other seafood, and for the Rhode Island greening, a greenish-skinned apple that is the prized ingredient of New England's green-apple pie.

While much of Connecticut's cropland is given over to the cultivation of shadeleaf tobacco, a tobacco used in cigar wrappers, its Long Island Sound shore is well planted with oyster beds. It is also famous for its shad fisheries, for its Block Island swordfish, for Connecticut coast lobsters, and for scallops and clams, as well as dairy and poultry products.

In speaking of the people of New England, we have mentioned so far only the Indians and the English, although even in early pre-Revolutionary days there were French Huguenots living in Maine. After the English colonists of the 1600s, however, the largest single migration into New England was that of the Irish, driven by famine from their homeland after the failure of the potato crop in 1846–47.

The last half of the 1800s saw the immigration of many European nationals—Italians, Portuguese (many of whom went into the fishing trades in Massachusetts port towns and on Cape Cod), Poles, Russians, Swedes, and Germans. Canadians, too, came into New England in great numbers.

In the regions where these newer Americans have settled, there have been subtle changes in the basic flavor of New England cookery. The Portuguese cook their fish with olive oil, tomatoes, and a pinch of garlic; the Irish have amended boiled dinners and come up with corned beef and cabbage, and Irish lamb stew with dumplings; and New England highways carry signs proclaiming pizzas and "grinders" (the local version of the Italian hero, or submarine, or "poor boy," sandwich).

As always, people plus place produce the cookery of a region. In New England, the English influence predominated. It is interesting to ponder as to what New England cookery would be like today had the Spanish, the French, or the Germans, instead of the English, landed at Plymouth in the year 1620.

NEW ENGLAND
RECIPES TO TRY

NEW ENGLAND CLAM CHOWDER

(Makes 6 first-course servings or 4 main-course servings)

1	7½-ounce can minced clams
4	tablespoons diced salt pork or bacon
1	medium onion, diced fine (about ½ cup)
1	cup pared cubed potatoes (½-inch cubes or smaller)

½   teaspoon salt
    Pinch white pepper
1½ cups milk
¼   cup light cream
1½ tablespoons milk
1   tablespoon flour

Drain the minced clams and save the liquid. In a large, heavy saucepan cook the diced salt pork or bacon over medium-high heat until crisp and brown. Remove crisp pieces, drain on absorbent paper, and set aside. To fat remaining in saucepan, add diced onion and cook until tender and golden. Add potatoes.

Pour reserved clam juice into measuring cup and add enough water to make 1 cup. Add to onions and potatoes with salt and pepper. Cover and simmer just until potatoes are tender, 10 to 15 minutes.

Add the 1½ cups of milk and the light cream. Stir the 1½ tablespoons of milk gradually into the tablespoon of flour and mix smooth. Add to chowder and bring very slowly to the boiling point, stirring constantly, but do not boil. Check seasoning, adding additional salt and pepper if desired.

The chowder is best if made several hours before serving, as the flavor improves on standing. To serve, reheat, ladle into cups or soup bowls, and garnish with the crisp salt pork or bacon cracklings. Good with oyster crackers or Pilot Crackers.

NEW ENGLAND CORN OYSTERS

(*Makes about 10*)

1   large egg
1   cup cooked or canned whole-kernel corn, well drained
¼   teaspoon salt
    Dash pepper
⅓   cup sifted all-purpose flour
    Fat for frying (vegetable shortening, oil, or bacon fat)

Break egg into a bowl and beat well. Add corn, salt, and pepper. Mix thoroughly. Stir in flour.

Heat enough fat in a large frying pan so that bottom of pan is well coated, about ⅛ inch deep. Drop corn mixture by tablespoonfuls into frying pan. Fry until golden brown on bottom, turn, and fry second side until golden brown.

Remove corn oysters and place on paper toweling to absorb excess fat. Serve hot.

Corn oysters were often served in New England as a main dish with maple sirup. They are delicious, however, with a meat course such as pot roast and gravy, or with chicken, broiled, fried, or roasted.

NEW ENGLAND INDIAN PUDDING

(4 to 5 servings)

2	cups milk
2	tablespoons yellow corn meal
3	tablespoons dark molasses
2	tablespoons butter
1	small egg, well beaten
4	tablespoons sugar
½	teaspoon ground cinnamon
¼	teaspoon ground ginger
	Pinch salt
½	cup cold milk

In the top of a double boiler, over direct heat, *scald* the 2 cups of milk (heat almost to boiling—tiny bubbles will appear at edge). Add the corn meal gradually, stirring constantly to prevent lumping. Add the molasses. Place the double-boiler top into its bottom section which has been filled to the watermark. Cook over boiling water, stirring the mixture until thickened, about 5 to 10 minutes. Remove pan from heat. Add the butter and let it melt.

In a mixing bowl combine the egg, sugar, cinnamon, ginger, and salt. Beat well. Add the hot mixture, a *little* at a time, stirring after each addition. Pour into a buttered 1-quart casserole or baking dish. Bake uncovered at 300 degrees, 35 to 40 minutes. Now pour the ½ cup of cold milk over the pudding and bake 20 minutes more.

Serve Indian Pudding warm or cold, with cream or with vanilla ice cream. (This pudding will "whey," or separate a little. Spoon some of the liquid from the bottom of the baking dish over each serving.)

THE MIDDLE ATLANTIC STATES

New York   Delaware

New Jersey   Maryland

Pennsylvania Washington, D.C.

Tender golden waffles, doughnuts, and crullers; creamy cottage cheese, tangy coleslaw, and brown salt-encrusted pretzels—all seem typically American foods to us. Yet we know that these foods were not found in the diet of the Algonquian or Iroquois Indians. They had to be brought to the New World (although in an earlier and somewhat different form) from Europe. For the foods mentioned above, as well as a great many others, we are particularly indebted to the Dutch, German, and English settlers of the Middle Atlantic States.

The area that makes up the middle states of our eastern seaboard is rich and varied. It is bounded in northern New York and Pennsylvania by the windy shores of two of the great lakes, Erie and Ontario, and it stretches south as far as Chesapeake Bay and gentle Tidewater Maryland. From the Atlantic Ocean on the east, it spans an ever-changing panorama and terrain, reaching to the very shores of the Ohio River.

The advantages of the irregular coastline, rich-soiled river valleys, moderate climate, and good rainfall were to make the settlements of the Middle Atlantic region comfortable and prosperous. This is not to say that busy well-fed New Amsterdam, thriving mercantile Philadelphia, or the bountiful farmlands of the Pennsylvania Germans came into being without many hardships and considerable determination and toil. However, the kindlier climate, the fuller natural resources, and the less harried backgrounds of the settlers

55

made life in the Middle Atlantic colonies easier than in the colonies of New England.

FOODS OF THE ALGONQUIAN AND IROQUOIS TRIBES

The Indians of the Middle Atlantic area were divided into the two great warring families of the Iroquois and the Algonquian, with each family made up of many tribes and covering great sweeps of the country.

The Algonquian (who also occupied New England) lived chiefly on the coastal plain, or eastern seaboard, of the Middle Atlantic region. Members of the Algonquian family included tribes like the Shinnecock and the Montauk, on Long Island; the Manhattans in what is now New York City; the Delaware (or Leni-Lenape, as they called themselves) of eastern Pennsylvania, New Jersey, and Delaware, and the Nanticoke of southern Delaware and Maryland. Many of the smaller tribes, such as the Manhattans and the Nanticokes, were really sub-tribes of the Delaware.

Like their Algonquian brothers to the north in New England, they grew corn, squash, and beans. Game for the Algonquians consisted chiefly of venison and of smaller animals such as squirrel and rabbit. As was customary with Indians throughout North America, the Algonquian tribes also cooked and ate fat dogs. An account by an early Dutch writer describes the Indians along the Hudson preparing such a feast after expertly skinning the animal with shells.

On Long Island and on the shores of Delaware Bay and Chesapeake Bay, the Algonquians had ample supplies of shellfish—clams, oysters, and crabs, including the fine delicately flavored blue crabs of Chesapeake Bay. Migratory wild duck, geese, swan, and other waterfowl were also plentiful in the bay areas.

In what is now New York harbor, the Indians were reported to have found enormous oysters and to have caught lobsters six feet long. In spring the Hudson River was alive with shad swimming upstream from the ocean to spawn. The Indians of the Middle Atlantic region also ate snapping

turtles. These rather terrifying creatures, often weighing 20 pounds or more, were caught in fresh-water ponds up and down the eastern seaboard. They were later to become the ingredient of Philadelphia snapper soup. Farther south, in the waters of Chesapeake Bay and in the salt marshes surrounding it, the diamondback terrapin, a salt-water turtle prized above all others for its delicious flesh, was a feast for the Indians.

Passenger pigeons were thought to have been the most numerous birds in North America at one time. As they traveled the eastern woodlands in their north-south migrations, they afforded the Middle Atlantic Indian a rich source of food. The passenger pigeon flew low in thick, sky-darkening formations, miles and miles long, descending at sunset to roost in the trees. So great was the combined weight of the roosting pigeons that they were reported to have broken heavy branches and even entire limbs off stout trees.

The individual passenger pigeon was about 16 inches long, red-breasted and with a tapering tail. His diet consisted chiefly of woodland foods—acorns, nuts, and seeds. He was not difficult to kill and even rocks thrown at the passing flocks would bring down a goodly number.

It is doubtful, however, that the Indian left to his own devices would have annihilated the passenger pigeon as the white man eventually did. For with the coming of the European settlers the pigeons began to be killed in great quantities, sometimes for food, but often quite senselessly and beyond necessity. Their numbers began to diminish and in 1914 a final single specimen of this variety of pigeon died in the Cincinnati Zoo, making the passenger pigeon extinct in the United States today.

Traveling farther inland through the Middle Atlantic region, we leave the coastal plain behind and come to a pleasant country of rolling hills and tilted saucer-shaped valleys. This terrain is known as the Piedmont, meaning literally "foot of the mountains." And if we continue westward we do indeed reach the mountains, the Allegheny ranges of central Pennsylvania and western Maryland.

Most of this region west of the coastal plain was held by the fierce and warlike Iroquois family, with the central and western portions of New York State their special stronghold. Here in the isolated highlands of the Adirondack Mountains, in the valley of the Mohawk River, and in the Finger Lakes region the Iroquois held sway.

Despite their bitterness and hostility toward the Algonquians, the Iroquois lived and ate in much the same fashion as their enemies, for both were the product of similar background, experiences, and geographical surroundings. In northern New York State, along the Vermont border, the Iroquois made maple sirup from the sap of the sugar maple just as the New England Algonquian Indians did. Early French travelers in the region reported being served dried popped corn with hot maple sirup poured over it. This early Iroquois confection was the forerunner of our Cracker Jack.

In the great forests deer, bear, and elk were game for the Iroquois, and wild turkey and grouse were plentiful. Buffalo roamed the south shore of Lake Erie, eating the prairie grass that grew on the wind-swept lowland. On the present site of the city of Buffalo were great salt licks that attracted the huge beasts in herds. The Iroquois of this region hunted the buffalo, using their hide as a source of clothing and shelter and their flesh for food. In this they had an advantage over the Algonquians, for the buffalo was seldom to be found east of these plains.

Wild strawberries grew on the shores of Lake Erie and Lake Ontario. Their juicy sparkling presence in the spring, after the long barren winter, spurred the Iroquois celebration known as the Strawberry Festival, a kind of thanksgiving for the yearly renewal of growth. Raspberries and blackberries, plums, cherries, grapes, and many varieties of nuts including walnuts, chestnuts, and butternuts—all came to fruition as the season progressed. And in the autumn, with the gathering of the harvest, the Iroquois held both a Bean Festival and a Corn Festival.

If history were not so full of accidents, the Hudson River might today be called the Verrazano, and Nieuw Amsterdam might have been settled by the French and known, perhaps, as the city of Nouveau Paris. For it was Giovanni da Verrazano, an Italian navigator in the employ of the French government, who first sailed into the magnificent wilderness harbor of New York in 1524.

THE DUTCH SETTLE NEW NETHERLAND

But Verrazano was not seeking forests, river valleys, rich farmlands, or even great new cities. He was looking for a route to Asia across the American continent, and his exploration of Delaware Bay, of the waters off Long Island, and of the river that was to become the Hudson did not lead to colonization by the indifferent French.

Eighty-five years later, in 1609, the navigator Henry Hudson, an Englishman sailing for the wealthy and enterprising Dutch East India Company, sailed up the river that was to bear his name in the gaily bedecked *Half Moon*. The brightly painted ship, alive and rustling with many-colored pennants, attracted the interest of the Indians along the Hudson shore who soon swarmed aboard to trade furs and tobacco for penknives, beads, bits of cloth, and a great deal more strong Holland gin than was good for them.

Although Hudson too was searching for the passage to Asia that he never found, the wealth of beaver, otter, and other furs to be obtained from the Indians soon brought Dutch traders to the lands along the Hudson. Forts that were used as trading posts were built as early as 1614, but it was not until 1623 that the ship *Nieuw Nederlandt* sailed for the New World with the first Dutch settlers, thirty families in all.

Even then, the Dutch were not wildly enthusiastic about settling in America. Times were prosperous in Holland and religious toleration was practiced. The harsh needs that drove the Pilgrims and the Puritans from the shores of England did not exist for the Dutch. Many of the settlers, once established in New Jersey, upriver near Albany, on Long Island, or on Manhattan Island itself, preferred fur trading to farming. However, with the arrival of more settlers and a shipload of livestock and farm implements in 1625, followed by the purchase of Manhattan Island from the Indians in 1626, the Dutch settlements of New Netherland began to take hold.

Although the Dutch governed their colony on the Middle Atlantic shore of the New World for only about forty years before the English took over in 1664, their influence was rich, colorful, and surprisingly enduring. New York City,

Long Island, the Hudson River Valley, Albany, and parts of New Jersey are full of Dutch place names and even a scattering of old Dutch buildings. Many of the foods of the Dutch have become such everyday items in our national diet that we are often apt to forget their European origin and their regional background here in America.

The Dutch were great grain and cereal lovers. Among the many hearty food traditions that they brought with them from Holland was a strong preference for porridges and puddings; breads of rye, whole grain or white wheat flour; dumplings, pancakes, and waffles; sweet cakes and cookies including doughnuts and crullers; and monstrous fruited and brandied wedding cakes, so huge that they had to be mixed in a washtub.

It was no surprise, therefore, that the Dutch took care to bring seeds of wheat and barley, rye and buckwheat, to the New World. They also brought farm implements and working livestock to aid in clearing the thickly forested lands of the river valleys. And in anticipation of their harvest, the Dutch even brought along the long-handled waffle irons on which to bake waffles in the fireplace.

THE BREADBASKET OF THE AMERICAN COLONIES

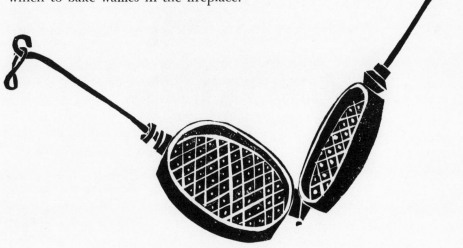

In none of these plans were they disappointed, for they had provided well and the land was perfectly suited to the crops. The rye and barley grew taller than a man, and the wheat was excellent. With their keen appreciation of cereal grains, the Dutch also took quickly to the Indian corn which they called "Turkey wheat." (This was a name for maize that was used in Holland. When Indian corn was first introduced there, many people erroneously supposed that it had been brought from Asia.) A favorite breakfast dish in New Amsterdam and throughout the colony of New Netherland was *suppawn*, a porridge of corn meal boiled in milk.

The pounding of the dried corn into meal was tiresome work, with the Dutch housewife at first using the Indian samp mortar as did her New England neighbor women to the north. But the Dutch had long experience in the milling of grains and they soon built windmills where wheat and rye

might be ground to flour, and the coarser corn into fine meal. Only in the outlying areas, such as the Long Island estates where Negro slaves were kept, did corn continue to be ground by hand.

The Dutch went even one step further in the production of breadstuffs. As early as 1656 there were public bakeries in New Amsterdam. When we consider that two hundred years later, almost to the close of the nineteenth century, 95 per cent of the bread in America was still being baked at home, we realize how advanced the Dutch were.

Moreover, laws were passed decreeing that bakeries could not sell cookies or other sweet cakes unless they also had bread for sale, and that they must bake "coarse" (whole grain) loaves as well as white loaves. Prices were also fixed by law, and they seem very reasonable even for Dutch colonial times. A two-pound white loaf could be had for eight cents in our equivalent of Dutch money, and the coarse bread, which was baked in huge loaves weighing up to eight pounds per loaf, was even cheaper.

Wisely, the authorities had even restricted the cultivation of tobacco, decreeing that a larger proportion of the land be given over to grain and other edible crops. Wheat, therefore, became the true wealth of New Netherland, while the fur trade, which had been its original promise of prosperity, began to decline. Wheat flour was sold to both the New England and the southern colonies, and continued to be a product of major importance long after New Netherland became New York. In the late 1700s New York was growing so much wheat that she was termed the "granary of the Revolution." It was not until 1850, when the vast wheatlands of the Midwest began to produce grain to feed the rapidly expanding nation, that New York State farmers turned to other pursuits.

THREE MEALS A DAY IN NEW AMSTERDAM Pictures of Dutch life in the fairy-tale village of New Amsterdam have been vividly preserved for us. Perhaps these images hold fast because no trace at all now remains of the steep-roofed houses with their weathervanes, their stiff little flower and vegetable gardens, their *stoeps* for sitting out of doors and chatting, their Dutch doors divided top from bottom to keep the geese from wandering in from the street.

Morning began in New Amsterdam with a draft of beer for all the family, as in New England, followed by a breakfast of *suppawn*, rye bread, and headcheese. Headcheese was not a cheese, but a type of sausage made of bits of cooked meat from the head and feet of a hog, mixed with vinegar and spices and pressed into the shape of a cheese.

The Dutch had brought good dairy stock with them from Holland and they made much butter and *smearcase* (cottage cheese) . Bread was lavishly buttered in New Amsterdam, for butter sold for as little as eight stivers a pound in Dutch money, or sixteen cents. Firm cheese was usually eaten grated rather than sliced or cut in wedges, and was a typical breakfast food. Buttermilk or more beer was drunk along with the meal.

Dinner, the big midday meal, often produced an array of rich and heavy foods. A favorite dish, derived from the *hutspot* of Holland, was a samp porridge of corn meal cooked with chunks of corned beef or salt pork and root vegetables such as carrots and turnips. The Dutch liked their American version of *hutspot* cooked slowly for three days, often until a thick crust formed and the entire meal could be lifted out of the pot in one piece. *Hutspot* really means hodgepodge, for almost any meat, cereal, or vegetable may be added to it.

On more festive occasions there were dishes such as pork with cabbage, roast duck with dumplings, and for holiday dinners, roast goose was almost a certainty. Every Dutch housewife had her flock of geese waddling through the lanes to the waterside, handy for making feather beds or for holiday feasting. For as little as fifteen stivers, or thirty cents, the Indians sold 30-pound haunches of venison for roasting,

often peddling their wares from door to door. Wild turkey, partridge, and passenger pigeons could also be purchased at reasonable prices by the town-dwelling Dutch.

Many varieties of fish were caught in the Hudson, but shad were so plentiful that only the poorer classes were not ashamed to be caught eating them. The salted shad of New Amsterdam were considered the equivalent of the common salt herrings of Holland, eaten with onions as a staple in the diet of the poor. Huge succulent lobsters and oysters were caught in New York Bay until the Revolutionary War, at which time the cannonading in the harbor, it is believed, drove them off forever. Delicious crabs dug on the sandy bay shores were described as having claws tinged with orange, white, and blue, the very colors of the Netherlands flag.

Supper in New Amsterdam was likely to be *suppawn* again. Or perhaps the main dish would be a hearty ham hock and split pea soup served with *koolslaa* (coleslaw), the shredded cabbage salad of Holland. For dessert there would be *oliekoeken*, sometimes spelled *olykoecks* or *olijkoecks*, the Dutch ancestors of the American doughnut. *Oliekoeken* (literally oil cakes) were made of yeast-raised dough shaped into little balls. A raisin or a bit of finely chopped apple was placed in the center, then the cakes were fried in deep hot lard until golden brown, rolled in sifted sugar, and served warm. The Pilgrims in New England also knew of *oliekoeken* from their twelve-year sojourn in Holland prior to coming to the New World. The doughnut of today, with the hole in the middle, was developed later to eliminate the sometimes soggy center and to give more crisp eating edges.

At the close of the day the children of the New Amsterdam household were put to bed with a soothing drink of warm beer or perhaps a mug of mulled (warmed and spiced) apple cider. Through the night the rattle-watch walked the streets with lantern, hourglass, and *klopper,* a large rattle which he shook at each passing door as reassuring evidence of his presence. On clouded nights, or during the dark of the moon, a lantern hung at the door of every seventh house to light the *klopperman*'s way.

THE DUTCH KITCHEN

In New Netherland, as in New England, the kitchen was the living heart of the home, for here was the huge brick fireplace faced with white-and-blue Dutch tiles. Alongside the fireplace, built into the fireplace wall, was the brick baking oven. From breakfast time at five or six o'clock in the morning to bedding-down time at eight or nine in the evening, the Dutch kitchen was the scene of unceasing bustle. Dinner was served here along about noon, with teatime falling anywhere between three and six. In between mealtimes, countless activities of which food preparation was but one took place in the ruddy warmth of the kitchen.

Friends and guests were most often entertained at teatime, and although most Dutch homes had a *kamer,* or parlor, stiffly furnished and used for weddings and funerals, the kitchen was sure to be the scene of that gay everyday sociality that the Dutch enjoyed so much.

Tea, chocolate, sugar, spices, dried fruits, wines, and brandies were all available to the Dutch at a time when New Englanders were still living chiefly on Indian corn and game. For Holland, although a small country, was a great mercantile power whose ships traded in all the richest ports of the world, and New Netherland had valuable pelts, lumber, and grain to exchange for these luxuries.

Both lump sugar and "granulated" sugar were offered with tea. The granulated sugar was not sifter-fine as ours is today, but was loaf sugar pounded into coarse uneven granules. None the less, the more prosperous tea tables of New Netherland were proud to display the little shell-shaped silver "bite and stir" boxes that held, in one compartment, lump sugar for biting and nibbling along with one's tea, and in the other compartment, pounded sugar to be stirred into the tea.

Oliekoeken, waffles, and other sweet cakes and cookies that went by the delightful names of jumbles, puffards, and wonders were all served with tea. Dutch apple cake, too, was a teatime accompaniment, the cake made of sweetened yeast dough and topped with apple slices sprinkled with sugar and cinnamon. In New Amsterdam a "tea-water pump" supplied a superior-tasting water that was purchased by wealthier families for brewing tea. Poorer folk used river water for making tea, for ordinary well water on Manhattan Island was the poorest-tasting of all.

Like the New England colonists, the Dutch kept large supplies of home-woven linen, including enormous table napkins, for washing was done infrequently and most food was taken with the fingers. While wooden trenchers were used, many of the Dutch colonists also had pewter porringers (soup or porridge bowls) and plates, platters and teapots of delftware (a decorated white pottery made in Delft, Holland). Spoons were of pewter or silver, and the wealth of a New Amsterdam burgher (town-dweller) could be gauged by the proportion of silver to pewter with which his wife set her table.

Since Dutch ships brought the first Negro slaves to the American colonies, setting them ashore in Virginia in 1619, it is not surprising that by 1625 or 1626 Negro slaves were being brought to New Netherland. As the colony expanded, estates heavily staffed with slaves were established on Long Island and in other country areas where there were extensive fields to be worked.

The average Dutch housewife, however, like her New England counterpart, did her own housework. She gave special attention to her kitchen, scouring and scrubbing it often, and following the Dutch custom of sprinkling the newly washed floor with clean sand. The Sabbath in New Netherland was a day of rest, even for the kitchen fireplace, which each Sunday had a freshly washed frilled valance hung across the top to signify that the week's cooking had come to an end.

DUTCH FESTIVALS AND OBSERVANCES

The hearty fun-loving Dutch needed little excuse for merry-making. A house raising, a barn raising, even work on a public building, called for frequent interruptions to partake of beer, cider, or brandy. Rum, although not so widely used as in New England, was nevertheless taken in goodly quantities by the New Netherlanders, especially at housewarmings, weddings, and other occasions for all-out feasting and drinking.

At funerals it was customary to sip Madeira wine and to eat *doed-koecks* at the home of the deceased. *Doed-koecks* (funeral cakes) were thick round cookies, about four inches in diameter, made with caraway seed. Often they were marked with the initials of the deceased and were taken home by the mourners and kept for years as mementos. *Doed-koecks* were usually baked at home, but there was a public baker in Albany who made these his specialty. It was also the custom at Dutch funerals to give gifts such as scarfs, gloves, handkerchiefs, and even rings or silver spoons to the pallbearers. If the deceased had been very wealthy, such gifts might be given to all the mourners. These items were usually inscribed with the initials of the departed and the date of his death.

Each season of the year offered sports and gay pastimes, from sleighing and skating parties in winter to strawberry picnics in summer. June was the wild-strawberry season on Long Island, the country folk from miles around driving into the fields with bottles of wine, and cream and sugar, to partake on the spot of the fresh-picked berries.

"Pulling the goose" was a rough but exceedingly popular sport in New Netherland. It consisted of reaching for a live greased goose from a swiftly moving rowboat. The goose was hung from a rope above the stream, and each contestant, standing on a plank laid across the stern of the boat, took a turn at the slippery goose as he passed beneath it. A miss resulted in the plank's tipping and the contestant's being dashed into the water. It is assumed that the winner, if there was one in such a chancy contest, was awarded the prize and enjoyed roast goose for dinner.

Bowling, too, was enormously popular in New Netherland. It was played out of doors on the lawn or green of a tavern where the men of the neighborhood congregated to drink, gamble, or discuss the news—hence the name bowling green. One of these bowling greens at the tip of Manhattan Island has actually been preserved and is today still identified by that place name.

Favorite holidays in New Netherland were New Year's Day and May Day. The delightful custom of calling on one's friends on New Year's can be traced to the Dutch. In a spirit of camaraderie and good cheer, friends and neighbors went visiting from house to house, where they were served wine, eggnog or punch, fruitcake, and sweet fried cakes, often in the formal grandeur of the parlor rather than in the kitchen.

May Day was again a time of visiting and drinking. A gaily decorated maypole was set up on the local green, and guns were fired to herald the incoming season.

At Shrovetide, the days immediately preceding Ash Wednesday and the beginning of the Lenten season, the Dutch housewife made *oliekoeken* so that family and friends might feast on the rich doughnuts before the onset of the Lenten fast. Making *oliekoeken* at Shrovetide had its practical aspects, too, for the frying of the sweet cakes used up the last of the lard which had been rendered the previous autumn and was not likely to keep through the warm months ahead.

Thanksgiving did not have the same significance for the Dutch as it did for the New England colonists and therefore was little celebrated in New Netherland.

Christmas was celebrated early, as the feast day of Saint Nicholas on December 6, the day of the good saint's death. Saint Nick, as he was affectionately called, actually lived in the fourth century and was a particular favorite in Holland where he was beloved by children as a bestower of gifts. In New Netherland he continued to play this role, tossing sweets and presents through the doorways of the Dutch houses as he passed through the streets accompanied by his servant. The role of the servant was often played by a Negro in the Dutch settlements of America.

The name of Saint Nicholas was eventually transformed through the prattle of excited youngsters into Santa Claus, making the Dutch of New Netherland largely responsible for the place he now holds in Christmas festivities in the United States. *St. Nikolaas koekjes* (Santa Claus cookies) spiced with cinnamon, nutmeg, and cloves were baked in honor of the well-loved saint. In the evening after the exhausted children had been put to bed, the table was laid with a white cloth and the grownups gathered round to drink chocolate punch and eat hot roasted chestnuts, as they sang songs of reverence to the "good holy man," Saint Nicholas.

Later in the month of December the Dutch made a solemn religious observance of the birth of Christ. It is only in quite modern times that the feast of Saint Nicholas has been moved from December 6 to merge with the religious holiday of the twenty-fifth.

**THE QUAKERS AND
THE GERMANS IN
PENNSYLVANIA**

Like the Pilgrims and the Puritans before them, the Quakers were a despised and persecuted religious sect in England. Their very name Quaker was given them by their enemies in mockery of their belief that men should tremble before the Lord.

Soon after the religion was founded, about 1648, many Quakers attempted to find a haven in the New World. But even in the colonies settled by other once-persecuted peoples the Quakers were not welcome. In many places they were whipped, fined, banished, even hanged. Massachusetts passed a law against Quakers in 1656.

To their very good fortune, the Friends, as the Quakers called themselves, had both a fellow religionist and an influential courtier in William Penn. In 1681, in payment of a debt owed to his father, Penn obtained a grant of land in America from the English king. This distant, unknown tract, almost as large as England and Wales, was a region of undreamed-of riches—mountains and rivers, mineral deposits of coal, iron, and petroleum, and thickly forested country that was to become fertile rolling farmland. This was Pennsylvania.

By 1685 the city of Philadelphia was a thriving community of narrow but regular rectangular streets faced with brick dwellings built in the style of London residences of the day. Most of the Quaker settlers were people of means, and they brought with them from England ample supplies of food-stuffs, clothing, tools, and other equipment. They got on extremely well with the Indians and soon learned to use Indian corn and corn meal in their cookery, as well as elk, venison, wild turkey, passenger pigeons, and waterfowl, all of which were plentiful in the region.

The snapping turtle became the central ingredient of Philadelphia snapper soup and of snapper-and-oyster stew. Salt pork, onions, and other vegetables were the basis of snapper soup, which contained turtle eggs and small chunks of turtle meat and was enriched with Portuguese Madeira wine, imported in trade with Spain.

Philadelphia was soon a center of commerce, receiving not only poultry, beef, mutton, dairy products, and farm vegetables of the nearby countryside, but also table luxuries of the world from abroad—rum, Madeira wine, preserved fruits, spices, coffee, chocolate, and tea. The tavern and coffee house of early Philadelphia served as stock exchange, newspaper, and club. Business involving costly cargoes, vessels, and crews was carried on at the tavern, and slaves were auctioned off before its door, while hearty, even lavish meals were served in its dining rooms. Great joints of meat were spit-roasted over open fires, rich steamed puddings were offered for dessert, and punches and wines were taken in liberal quantity.

Philadelphia pepper pot was the soup of the American Revolution. It is said to have been improvised for General George Washington's troops at Valley Forge. With his men cold and hungry, their spirits at lowest ebb, General Washington urged his cook to prepare an emergency ration of some hot, filling dish. Having only some tripe—the gift of a Philadelphia butcher—and a handful of peppercorns, the inventive cook put together the soup called pepper pot which was reported to have met with great approval.

Philadelphia pepper pot is always made with tripe, the lining of the stomach of a cow or other cud-chewing animal. Honeycomb tripe, the lining of the second stomach, is marked with small ridges patterned like the cells of a honeycomb and is preferred in pepper pot because of its more delicate flavor and texture. The tripe is cut in small cubes and is simmered with onions, potatoes, and other vegetables. Crushed or pounded peppercorns give the soup its hearty bite and zesty flavor. In Philadelphia during the 1800s Negro woman vendors went through the streets selling pepper pot, their approach heralded by the familiar call, "Peppery pot, smokin' hot!"

Philadelphia sticky buns are another food specialty of the City of Brotherly Love. These little sweet rolls are probably descended from the *schnecken* (cinnamon rolls) of the German people who came as early as 1682 to settle in Germantown, now a part of the city of Philadelphia. Sticky buns are

made of yeast-raised dough, sprinkled with sugar, cinnamon, chopped walnuts, raisins, and perhaps other dried fruits such as citron or currants. The sheet of dough is then rolled up and sliced into little snail shapes which are baked in a mixture of brown sugar and honey or sirup.

The Germans who came to Pennsylvania from 1682 on were members of numerous religious sects. One of the largest of these was the Mennonites, who were sometimes referred to as the German Quakers. Most of the German settlers spread out into the wilderness area surrounding Philadelphia, which they soon transformed into farmlands of unsurpassed bounty. Some remained in Philadelphia, and Philadelphia scrapple can be traced to their influence.

Scrapple was the wedding of German sausage-making skills to American Indian corn meal. It was usually made at hog-slaughtering time to use up pork scraps, hence its name. To make scrapple, pork trimmings are cooked in water, chopped fine, and seasoned with salt, pepper, sage, and other spices. Corn meal is then added to the meat and simmering broth, and cooked to a thick mush. The scrapple is cooled in greased oblong forms. At breakfast time scrapple is sliced thin and fried on the skillet to a crisp, golden brown. It is served with poached eggs, fried apples, applesauce or simply with brown-sugar sirup. Scrapple could not be stored for long in the early days as it did not keep well. Today, however, it is sold in cans and can be kept on the pantry shelf for a Philadelphia-style Sunday breakfast at a few moments' notice.

Philadelphia pepper relish is also a by-product of Pennsylvania German cookery, which is noted for its "sweets and sours," pickles and preserves of vegetables and fruits that add sparkle to hearty German meals. The famous pepper relish is a mixture of chopped red and green peppers plus shredded cabbage, diced celery, and onions pickled in vinegar, spices, and brown sugar. It is served with meats as a tangy salad.

Philadelphia ice cream has always been noted for its purity and simple goodness. It differs from French ice cream in which egg yolks are used for thickening, and from other ice creams which are prepared with flour, cornstarch, or other thickening agents. Philadelphia ice cream originated as a frozen mixture of cream, sugar, and vanilla flavoring, nothing more. It was this purely American version of ice cream that Dolly Madison served at the White House in Washington, D.C., in the early 1800s.

Pennsylvania was so tolerant and open a colony that it very soon contained, in addition to the English Quakers and Germans of various religious sects, Welshmen, Scotch-Irish, and the very Church of England countrymen who had so bitterly opposed the Quakers back home in England. Swedes, too, who had dwelt along the Delaware River in Pennsylvania before the arrival of William Penn and the Quakers, had been absorbed into the population. Unlike the cities of Boston or New Amsterdam, which remained almost purely English or purely Dutch long enough to establish a strong regional cookery, Philadelphia became, quite early in its history, a blend of influences.

However, for a distinct regional cookery that has remained almost unchanged from about 1700 to the present, one need only travel a short distance west or northwest from Philadelphia. Here lies the country of the Pennsylvania *Deutsch* (Pennsylvania Germans) whose Quaker neighbors mistook *Deutsch* for Dutch, and hence misnamed them the Pennsylvania Dutch. Knit together by strong family and religious ties that reject many aspects of modern civilization, these people have preserved a way of life that is both simple and dignified—and a rich regional cookery as well.

THE "WONDERFUL GOOD" FOOD OF THE PENNSYLVANIA DUTCH

The homely colorful expressions of the Pennsylvania Dutch tell us a great deal about how these Americans of German origin feel about food: "Eat yourself full." . . . "Come on in and shovel yourself out." . . . "No woman can be happy with less than seven to cook for."

Plain and plenty might best describe the character of Pennsylvania Dutch cookery. Pot-roasted meats and stews were among the most basic dishes to be transplanted, almost without change, from the farms and villages of Germany to the newly cleared woodlands of Pennsylvania. *Sauerbraten* (sweet-and-sour pot roast), *boova shenkel* (beef stew with potato dumplings), and *hinkel bot boi* (chicken pot pie) have remained favorite main dishes to this day in the Pennsylvania Dutch country.

For *sauerbraten* the beef must be marinated, or soaked, in a mixture of vinegar and spices for two to five days before cooking. The meat is then well browned on all sides, in a deep heavy pot, and simmered in the marinade until tender. Carrots and onions may be added to the pot to cook along with the beef. For a final touch, a generous handful of crushed gingersnaps is added to thicken the gravy and give a sweet spicy tang to the pot roast.

Boova shenkel translates literally as "boys' legs" rather

than beef stew. Fat, half-moon dumplings stuffed with mashed potato are cooked atop a simmering stew of beef and gravy. At the very last the entire dish is smothered in a sauce of browned bread cubes in milk and served steaming hot. The resemblance of the dumpings to the chubby legs of a small boy gives the dish its pet name.

Noodles, as well as dumplings, form a substantial part of many Pennsylvania Dutch dishes. *Hinkel bot boi* consists of chunks of tender chicken and very broad noodles swimming in a golden creamy sauce and topped with a flaky browned pie crust.

Dumplings turn up again in *schnitz un knepp* (apples and dumplings), probably the most famous of all Pennsylvania Dutch specialties. *Schnitz* are sliced, dried sweet apples (the word *schnitz* meaning a slice). From the time of the first apple harvest in the new land, thrifty Pennsylvania Dutch housewives have been drying apple slices for year-round use.

Schnitz un knepp begins with a thick slice of ham boiled in water until nearly tender. (A thriftier version uses simply a ham bone, for flavor.) Next the dried apple slices and some brown sugar are added. Lastly, the dumpling batter is dropped by spoonfuls into the pot. The pot cover goes on tight and no peeking allowed until the proper cooking time of about twenty minutes elapses. Then off with the lid, and the steaming dish of tender smoky ham, plump sweet apple slices, and feathery dumplings is ready to be served.

Schnitz may also be prepared with pears, the fruit sliced and dried exactly as with apples. Pears are sometimes used instead of apples in *schnitz un knepp*. A favorite drying method was to place the cut fruit in the slowly dying heat of the baking oven. The early Pennsylvania Dutch settlers built huge outdoor ovens of stone. The interiors of these ovens were sometimes seven feet wide and could accommodate five or six loaves of bread, seven or eight pies, half a dozen crumb cakes, and several batches of cookies all at the same time! A six-foot-long baker's shovel was used to extract the fragrant baked goods.

Corn has always yielded an abundant crop in the Pennsylvania Dutch country, and just as with apples, pears, and other fruits, it was the housewife's way to dry the harvested corn for use throughout the winter months. To dry sweet corn, the kernels were cut from the ripe ears and dried in a very slow oven, or out of doors in the sun on a cloth-covered screen suspended from wooden posts.

Dried sweet corn, also known as sugar corn, is soaked over-night, then simmered in water until tender and served in butter and cream. It is also used in *hinkel welschkarn suup* (chicken corn soup), a rich chicken broth swimming with tender kernels of sugar corn. Nowadays both *schnitz* and dried sugar corn are put up in cellophane bags and offered for sale throughout the Pennsylvania Dutch country.

Rivel soup is another Pennsylvania Dutch specialty. *Rivels* are tiny specks of dough made by rubbing flour, salt, and egg together until crumbly, then tossing the crumbles into boiling chicken or beef broth. When cooked, the *rivels* look a little bit like boiled rice.

Pretzels are everywhere in the Pennsylvania Dutch coun-try, so it is not surprising that pretzel soup should be a favorite supper-time dish. Pretzel soup is the easiest dish in the world to put together. Each member of the family re-ceives a bowl of hot milk with butter melted in it. Then he breaks up enough large soft pretzels to fill the bowl.

Pretzels have a long and interesting history that goes all the way back to the time of the Crusades. The shape of the twisted pretzel is said to symbolize the position of the arms crossed in prayer. The Pilgrims were able to string pretzels onto their staffs, providing themselves with a long-keeping type of bread that could be eaten as they journeyed from place to place.

The Germans and the Austrians brought the art of pretzel-making to the New World. Large soft pretzels are best eaten freshly baked and still slightly warm; crisp dry pretzels keep almost indefinitely. Twisting pretzels by hand is a skill that is not as easy as it looks. During the 1860s when the first commercial pretzel bakeries were established all pretzels were hand twisted, but expert pretzel-twisters received only one penny per tray of sixty pretzels! The brown glaze that makes pretzels appear so tempting is not natural to them. It is achieved by coating the biscuit-toned pretzels with a harmless chemical solution before baking.

The people of the Pennsylvania Dutch country have many colorful superstitions. "Hex" signs decorate their barns to ward off evil spirits. At table, particularly at a company or holiday meal, there must be exactly "seven sweets and seven sours," a dazzling array of appetite-sparking pickles and preserves. Among the sweets there is likely to be apple butter; pickled watermelon rind; spiced seckel pears; lemon honey; and jams, jellies, and marmalades made from quince, rhubarb, cherry, and other fruits. The sours are sure to include corn relish, pepper relish, green tomato relish, sweet pickles, dill pickles, marinated vegetables, and pickled hard-cooked eggs and beets, the eggs dyed a sizzling red by the spiced beet juice in which they have been marinating for two days.

Apple butter is as traditional as *schnitz* in the Pennsylvania Dutch country. It is not a dairy product, but a smooth rich fruit spread, very much like a jam. The making of apple butter was an outdoor community activity in the early days of settlement. The fresh apples were first cut up into small chunks and cooked in water until soft and pulpy. Then the pulp was pressed through a sieve and cooked in huge kettles over open fires with apple cider, sugar, and spices such as cinnamon, allspice, and cloves. The kettles were stirred with long wooden paddles until the mixture had cooked down, or thickened and the consistency was just nice and "buttery." Then the hot butter was ladled into jars, sealed, and stored for use all through the year until the next apple harvest. Bees (working get-togethers) for the making of apple butter and *schnitz* and for cornhusking were all important social activities in the lives of the Pennsylvania Dutch settlers.

Schmierkaes (the German name for cottage cheese) is often eaten with apple butter, the one spread thickly atop the other on homemade bread, at suppertime or snacktime. *Koppli kaes* (cup cheese) is an unusual tasting homemade cheese of pale yellow. It is prepared from ripened or fermented cottage cheese, has a thick, smooth, slightly runny consistency, and is served, for this reason, in small cups. Its flavor, although mild, takes some gettting used to. Both *schmierkaes* and *koppli kaes* are sometimes served with appetizer or relish courses at large dinners.

Pies are so much a part of Pennsylvania Dutch eating that it is not unusual for the housewife to bake up to two dozen a week (and many more in harvest season): *schnitz* pie (filled with cooked dried apple slices), raisin pie, lemon sponge pie, and of course, shoo-fly pie.

Raisin pie is also known as "funeral pie," for it was traditionally served along with a nourishing meal to mourners who had come a long distance to attend a funeral. Lemon sponge pie has an interesting filling, moist and puddinglike on bottom, spongy and cakelike on top.

Shoo-fly pie reveals the Pennsylvania Dutch knack for making much out of little when necessity demands it. The pie is probably descended from German crumb cake, sweetened in the New World with molasses because of the shortage of sugar. Then for extra heartiness the entire mixture was turned into a pie shell.

Remarkably enough, shoo-fly pie filling does not require eggs, milk, cheese, or fruit. Its principal ingredients are molasses and flour. Thus it was a great favorite in late winter when fresh fruits were not available and the *schnitz* and other dried fruits of the previous summer had been used up.

To make shoo-fly pie, the molasses mixture and the flour, or crumb, mixture are added to the pie shell in varying proportions to give the desired kind of pie. A dry shoo-fly pie has less molasses and is really more like a coffee cake baked in a pie shell. It is usually eaten at breakfast time, cut in large wedges and dunked in coffee. The main course at such a meal would probably be scrambled eggs, fried apples, and scrapple (which is called *ponhaus* by the Pennsylvania Dutch).

The wet shoo-fly pie has lots of molasses in the filling and is most often eaten as dessert. It is delicious, although not very traditional, served with whipped cream or vanilla ice cream. The patches of sticky molasses peeping through the crumb topping were always an attractive stopping place for the flies that hovered near the open windows of the farmhouse kitchen, hence the name *shoo-fly*.

Streusel kuchen (crumb cake), *schnecken* (cinnamon rolls), and *semmeln* (sugar-sprinkled sweet rolls, made with yeast-leavened mashed-potato dough) are all well-loved *kaffeeklatsch* (coffee-hour) offerings, served warm and fragrant in the big Pennsylvania Dutch kitchens. *Fastnachts* (Pennsylvania Dutch doughnuts) were originally made only on Shrove Tuesday, the eve of the Lenten fast, to use up the

fats in the household and to signify the end of rich eating. So impatient were the Pennsylvania Dutch children who had to wait a whole year for Fastnacht Day that these sweet fried cakes came to be made often throughout the year.

Thanksgiving and Easter are heartily celebrated, but Christmas dinner is almost certain to be the climax of all Pennsylvania Dutch feasting for the year. The main dish is likely to be duck with sauerkraut, or roast goose, preceded by *rivel* soup, goose livers in jelly, *schmierkaes* and home-made *koppli kaes*. Potato pancakes or hot potato salad, corn pudding, and green beans with vinegar, dressing and bacon are typical vegetable accompaniments—and of course there will be "seven sweets and seven sours" on the table. For dessert, two or three kinds of pie may grace the table, as well as an assortment of Christmas cookies including tiny round *pfeffernuesse* (spice nuts) and fancy-shaped *lebkuchen* frosted with tinted sugar icing.

It has been said of the thrifty yet bountiful Pennsylvania Dutch that they would have no difficulty at all making stone soup, and that moreover it would be nourishing and delicious. The recipe goes as follows. Simply take a large, smooth round stone from the fields, scrub it well, and place it in a large pot. Add water, carrots, onions, potatoes, salt, and pepper. Cook until done and serve steaming hot!

MARYLAND EASTERN SHORE COOKERY

Maryland, the most southerly of the Middle Atlantic States, is split nearly in two by Chesapeake Bay. On the eastern shore of the bay Maryland shares a peninsula with Delaware and with a tiny segment of Virginia, which is located at the southerly tip. This entire finger of land is today called the Delmarva Peninsula, drawing its name from the three states that comprise it. From the western shore of the bay Maryland sweeps northwestward, the land rising from the Tidewater (or coastal plain) to the Allegheny Mountains in the extreme western part of the state.

It was on the shores of Chesapeake Bay, however, that the

first English settlements were made in 1634 on a grant of land given by the English king to Lord Baltimore. To this section of Maryland, English gentlemen of means, most of them Catholics, emigrated in style. They built manor houses very much like the handsome plantation houses of Tidewater Virginia to the south of them. Slaves were imported to work in the tobacco fields, and a lavish social and sporting life, patterned after that of the landed aristocracy in England, was soon under way. Fox hunting, coaching parties, horse racing, and gracious prolonged entertaining were much-indulged pastimes.

On the Eastern Shore a rich regional cookery grew up, combining English influences, Negro cooking skills, and the natural food resources of Chesapeake Bay and the surrounding woodland area. Wild turkey and venison were served up as great succulent roasts along with native sweet potatoes and wild strawberries, as well as imported Spanish wines and steamed English puddings. The dinner table was always well attended by family, extensive household staff, and overnight or longer-staying guests.

Oyster stuffing for roast turkey was to become traditional in Maryland, for the vast bay offered a rich supply of these shellfish. Maryland oyster chowder and Maryland fried oysters soon became famous, and even as late as the 1800s Chesapeake Bay oysters were still so plentiful that they were set forth with meats, cheeses, pretzels, and other snack foods on the free-lunch counters of Baltimore bars.

Chesapeake Bay blue crab is renowned as the ingredient of Maryland cream of crab soup, golden-crusted Baltimore crab cakes, and deviled crab, Baltimore style. The deviled crab is a mixture of tender sweet crabmeat blended with hot seasonings such as mustard, Worcestershire sauce, and cayenne pepper. It is then topped with buttered crumbs and browned in the oven in scallop shells or individual ramekins (baking dishes).

Soft-shell crabs are not a different variety of crab but simply crabs that have recently shed their shells. As the crab grows, his hard shell becomes too small for his body and must be replaced by a new larger shell. Even in full-grown crabs this shedding process takes place every three or four years. The new-growing shell begins as a thin, delicate, translucent covering. Soft-shell crabs are delicious fried, and may be eaten shell and all.

Most highly prized of all Chesapeake Bay seafood is the diamondback terrapin, a salt-water turtle so named because of the diamond-shaped formation of the bony scales on its upper shell. At one time terrapin were so plentiful in the salt marshes along the shores of Chesapeake Bay that slave owners were forbidden to feed their slaves terrapin more than three times a week because of the cruel monotony of such a diet. But by the late 1800s terrapin had become scarce, and terrapin soup and terrapin stew were gourmet dishes to be found only in the most elegant and fashionable restaurants.

Although colonial life on the Eastern Shore of Maryland strongly resembled the plantation life of Virginia and other Southern colonies, the central or Piedmont portion of the state was to be settled from 1732 on by Pennsylvania Germans from just across her northern border. Maryland thus developed characteristics of both the North and the South. Although her Eastern Shore cookery was strongly Southern, and she was a slaveholding state, it is interesting to note that in the great conflict of the Civil War, Maryland remained loyal to the Union.

Although Washington, D.C., was primarily designed as a seat of government, she has, like all other cities, a culinary history of her own. The entertainment of visitors from both home and abroad has been the occasion, from Washington's earliest days, for many a glittering reception or formal state dinner.

It is too bad that the first President did not hold office in the present national capital, for that first of *all* first ladies, Martha Washington, was an excellent hostess. She is said to have possessed one of the first cookbooks in America, a notebook of hand-written recipes given to her by Mrs. Custis, the mother of her first husband Daniel Parke Custis. The dinners Martha Washington gave at Mount Vernon and later, when George Washington was President, are famous, and she was particularly noted for having advanced the art of preparing fruit and custard "pyes." These sweet pies, which were served as desserts, were a great departure from the meat "pyes" and main-course pastries of England.

However, Washington, D.C., was not readied for governmental use until 1800, and of George Washington's eight years in office (1789–97) the first was spent in New York and the remaining seven in Philadelphia. John Adams, the second President, spent his final year in office in Washington, D.C., but it was Thomas Jefferson, inaugurated in 1801, who was the first President to serve a full term in the White House.

Jefferson was a man of many talents and interests. From 1785 to 1789 he was Minister to France at the court of Louis XVI. He was much impressed with the French cuisine and on his return he introduced some of the refinements of French cookery to America, including blancmange (a delicate milk pudding) and meringues (confections of stiffly beaten egg whites and sugar). Jefferson kept a French steward and a French chef at the White House, but it is interesting to note that he had his own Negro cook from Monticello prepare breakfasts of bacon and eggs, fried apples, and the Virginia hot breads of which he was so fond.

GOOD EATING IN THE NATION'S CAPITAL

Jefferson's wife had been dead nineteen years when he became President, and Dorothy Todd Madison, the wife of James Madison, who was then Secretary of State, frequently acted as official hostess at the White House. She continued to serve in this capacity during Jefferson's second term.

When James Madison became President in 1809, it was the same Dolly Madison, by then a brilliant and beloved Washington hostess, who delighted her guests by making ice cream the "official" dessert at White·House dinners. Because of Dolly Madison's influence heavy desserts like puddings and pastries began to decline in importance, and macaroons and other small cakes accompanied the serving of the ice cream.

Ice cream was not a new food (frozen desserts were known in Italy as early as 1600), but it was still fairly new to America and its popularity was firmly established by the Washington hostesses who followed Queen Dolly's lead. Even casual visitors at the White House were served refreshments during Dolly Madison's regime. Punch and seedcake (made with caraway seeds and brandy, and flavored with nutmeg and mace) were customarily offered. Mrs. Madison also made it a practice to serve hot bouillon to guests on cold blustery afternoons.

Washington pie was a dessert improvised during the Civil War when Washington, D.C., housewives were unable to get lard for pie crusts. Like Boston cream pie, it wasn't a pie at all, but a spongecake baked in a pie pan or other shallow pan and split into two layers. The bottom layer was spread with jelly and the top layer lightly sprinkled with powdered sugar.

In the well-known restaurant of the United States Senate certain specialties of the house have long been favorites of both regular diners and visitors: U. S. Senate salad, Senate rum pie, and above all, U. S. Senate bean soup. This last is a concoction of white beans, vegetables, and ham bones, which are added for flavor. The recipe for this soup follows closely in the early American tradition of cooking with one of our most nourishing and abundant staples, dried beans.

Because Washington, D.C., is built on territory that once

belonged to Maryland, and because of its access to the waters
of Chesapeake Bay, blue crab in all its delicious guises, and
other local seafood as well, may be found often on Washington menus.

New York City has been called the melting pot of the nations.
She is also the cooking pot of the world, for immigrants from
lands too numerous to mention have come to this city to
live. Many of them have created communities of their own
within the city, like Little Italy and Chinatown in lower
Manhattan and the German, Czech, and Hungarian York-
ville in upper Manhattan. Scattered throughout the five
boroughs, on a less formal scale perhaps, are Greek, Jewish,
Scandinavian, Irish, Puerto Rican, and many other nation-
ality-based neighborhoods.

FOODS AND PEOPLE OF THE MIDDLE ATLANTIC STATES TODAY

New York City's restaurants are a reflection of the variety
of her people. It is possible to eat in almost any language in
New York City, from Algerian to Viennese, and in most
cases the food is both authentic and appetizing.

What, however, are some typical New York City foods? To
the *koolslaa, smearcase,* and *oliekoeken* of the 1600s have
been added creations of later eras. With an increase in her
wealth and worldliness, New York City in the late 1800s produced a dazzling array of dining establishments: Delmonico's
in 1861, and Louis Sherry's which opened in 1881 as an
elegant tearoom in the Metropolitan Opera House. Here
Sherry's served ice creams and pastries between the acts and
later, in 1890, opened its own restaurant and ballroom at
another location. In 1893 the Waldorf, located on fashionable
lower Fifth Avenue, opened its doors.

Several famous dishes were to be developed in these fine
restaurants. To celebrate the purchase of Alaska in 1867,
Delmonico's created baked Alaska, an ice-cream dessert that
is actually baked in the oven. The trick of baked Alaska is
to place the ice cream, which has been frozen firmly into
brick form, on a sheet of spongecake, then completely to

cover both cake and ice cream with a thick layer of meringue. The ice cream remains well insulated against the heat while the meringue browns quickly in a hot oven. The result is a golden hot fluffy meringue that blends perfectly with the cold creamy filling.

Lobster Newburg was another of Delmonico's creations, prepared especially to please a patron of the establishment. It is a rich mixture of lobster meat in a sauce of butter, sherry wine, cream, and egg yolks, often served on toast points or in shells of crisp, flaky puff paste.

The most New York dish of all to be brought forth during this era was the Waldorf salad. It was presented by Oscar of the Waldorf (the famous chef, Oscar Tschirky) at a society banquet given in 1893 to celebrate the opening of the Waldorf Hotel. The salad was a mixture of diced apples and celery tossed in a mayonnaise dressing and served in lettuce cups. A little later chopped walnuts were added to the mixture, and modern versions even include crushed or cubed pineapple.

Oysters were popular during the 1890s, and oyster bars and oyster houses flourished in New York City right on through the turn of the century. They featured Long Island oysters served either raw on the half shell, or in oyster stew. Manhattan clam chowder was another seafood house specialty. Unlike the original New England version of this dish, the Manhattan chowder contains tomatoes and other vegetables and is made without milk or cream.

Long Island is a rich source of fish and seafood, including scallops and clams, as well as oysters. Scallop shells from Long Island scallops serve so well as small baking dishes that they are responsible for those creamed foods and other mixtures known as scalloped dishes.

The largest duck farms in the country are on Long Island, but the famous ducklings produced there are not native to the region. They are descended from a variety of duck imported from Peking, China, in 1872. Long Island produces a variety of vegetables and fruits, and is especially noted for its potatoes, cauliflower, and strawberries.

In upstate New York the superb grapes of the Finger Lakes

region have given rise to an extensive wine industry. New York State champagnes rate high among domestic and even imported wines. Apples and sour cherries are also grown in abundance. New York State's cheese-making industry and maple-sirup production rival that of neighboring Vermont. Buckwheat is grown so extensively that New York State is said to have originated buckwheat cakes. These nut-flavored griddle cakes are made from a combination of buckwheat and other flours and are a breakfast favorite throughout the northeast, especially when doused with New York State or Vermont maple sirup.

New Jersey has been named the Garden State because of its excellent fruit and vegetable output. This state has a peculiar history, for it began as two separate and far-flung colonies, known as East Jersey and West Jersey. East Jersey, which lay directly across the Hudson River from New Amsterdam, was settled by the Dutch. Later, when New Amster-

dam became New York, Englishmen, Scotsmen, French
Huguenots, and even New Englanders swelled the population of East Jersey. West Jersey began as a Quaker settlement on the shores of the lower Delaware in 1674, seven
years before the Quakers obtained Pennsylvania.

Between the two settled areas lay a wilderness of thickets,
swamps, and pine barrens. The barrens were not treeless
places, but thick, very ancient forests of first-growth pine.
These almost impenetrable wastes made direct communication between the two settlements impossible. Nor was New
Jersey's Atlantic seacoast inviting to settlers, for it had few
safe harbors and was approachable only by careful navigation
through dangerous shoals.

Thus the Jersey settlements continued to cluster near the
mouths of the Hudson and the Delaware, and New York and
Philadelphia were the principal cities to serve as export
centers for the Jerseys' wheat and timber. No large cities
developed in the Jerseys during early colonial times. In 1702

the two Jerseys were united as a single colony under the British crown, but it was to be many years before the rough interior was subdued for farming.

This incredibly fertile area, most of it coastal plain, is now the source of New Jersey blueberries and bog-grown cranberries, of tomatoes, asparagus, sweet potatoes, corn, apples, peaches, and a thriving poultry industry. The New Jersey shore has a well-developed fishing industry with clams, oysters, sea bass, porgy, and fluke ranking high among the plentiful catch.

Pennsylvania has attracted people from a wide variety of foreign lands, beginning with the Swedes and the Finns who in the 1640s built their stout log cabins along the shores of the Delaware. They were followed in 1682 by the English Quakers under William Penn and soon after by the Germans, the Welsh, and the Scotch-Irish.

From the 1800s on, the anthracite areas and the steel mills brought Italian, Polish, Russian, Lithuanian, Hungarian, and Yugoslav workers to Pennsylvania. Like the hex signs and stone farmhouses of the Pennsylvania Dutch country, the anthracite region, too, has its symbols—the *kielbasa* (smoked sausage) and the polka music of the Slavic peoples, and, dotting the skylines of many of its towns, the onion steeples of the Russian Orthodox Church.

Grains such as wheat, rye, buckwheat, and corn are grown in Pennsylvania. Apples are an important fruit crop in the southeastern portion, and grapes are grown in the extreme northwestern section near Lake Erie.

Lebanon bologna is a famous smoked beef sausage of the Pennsylvania Dutch country. It was originally made at beef-butchering time by the Pennsylvania Dutch farmers of Lebanon County and is now sold commercially. It can be purchased by the piece in the cotton stockinette bag in which it was smoked, or simply sliced to order. The secret of Lebanon bologna's delicious flavor and long-keeping quality lies in the choice of spices that are blended with the beef and in the long slow smoking process over a fire of hickory and other fragrant woods.

Reading, Pennsylvania, is a large commercial pretzel-baking center. The fine flavor of its pretzels is attributed to the excellent spring waters of the area. The town of Hershey, Pennsylvania, is, of course, synonymous with the scent and the taste of chocolate.

Although the Dutch laid claim to Delaware because of Henry Hudson's exploration of Delaware Bay in 1609, it was the Swedes who first really settled this next to smallest state in the Union. Strangely enough their leader was Peter Minuit, who in 1626 had purchased Manhattan Island for the Dutch from the Indians.

In 1631 Minuit had been dismissed as governor of New Amsterdam and he was, no doubt, still smarting from this blow when he went into the service of the Swedish government. Although Minuit knew that the Dutch had fur-trading posts in Delaware, he guided the Swedish expedition to this very place.

Here in 1638 the Swedes purchased land from the Indians which they named New Sweden, and established the town of Fort Christina near the present site of Wilmington. Although the Dutch considered the Swedish settlers trespassers, the Swedes pursued their fur trading and farming until 1655 when the Dutch officially took over. In 1664, when the English took New Amsterdam, Delaware, being a Dutch possession, also fell to the English.

In Delaware today there are descendants of Swedish, Dutch, and English settlers, as well as Finns, French Huguenots, Scotch-Irish, and Quakers. The state is named after Thomas West, Lord De La Warr, first governor of Virginia.

Apples, peaches, strawberries, and melons are important Delaware fruit crops. Sweet potatoes, Irish potatoes, tomatoes, peas, and limas are also grown for market. The poultry industry is a flourishing one, with Delaware one of the sponsors of the Delmarva Chicken Festival. This is an annual chicken-cooking contest held under the auspices of the poultry growers of Delaware, Maryland, and Virginia, the three states that share the Delmarva Peninsula.

Maryland, Delaware's neighbor to the south and west, is prominent in turkey production as well as other phases of poultrying. Dairying is also an important industry. Canta-

loupes, popularly known as "lopes," are an abundant mid-summer crop, often offered for sale at roadside stands during July and August. Sweet potatoes, strawberries, peaches, asparagus, and spinach are grown extensively in the coastal plain region. Corn, wheat, and other grains are grown throughout the state, and excellent apples are produced in the Piedmont region. Probably most famous of all Maryland produce, however, is that of Chesapeake Bay—sweet soft-shell clams, succulent oysters, and delicate meaty blue crabs.

U. S. SENATE BEAN SOUP

(6 servings)

1	cup small navy pea beans
4	cups boiling water
	Ham bone with some meat on it, or thick piece of ham (¼–½ pound)
1	tablespoon butter
1	medium-sized onion, diced fine
1½	teaspoons salt
¼	teaspoon pepper

Wash the beans, cover them with cold water, and let soak overnight. Next day drain off water. In a large soup pot, bring 4 cups of water to a boil. Add the beans and the ham bone or piece of ham. Cover and simmer for 1 hour.

Meantime melt the butter in a small skillet. Add the onions and *sauté* (fry lightly), just until golden. When the soup has cooked for 1 hour, add the onions and simmer ½ hour more. Remove ham bone or ham piece. Put half the beans and half the liquid from the soup mixture through a coarse sieve and return to soup pot. Cut ham into small pieces, removing all bone and fat, and add to soup. Add salt and pepper, adjusting seasoning if necessary. Reheat to serve.

This recipe is adapted from that of the United States Senate Restaurant, where Bean Soup is a tradition and appears daily on the menu.

PENNSYLVANIA DUTCH SHOO-FLY PIE

(one 8- or 9-inch pie)

1   8- or 9-inch unbaked pie shell (Use a commercially prepared pie shell, make up pastry from commercial mix, or use own favorite recipe.)

Crumb Mixture:

1½   cups sifted all-purpose flour
½   cup light brown sugar, firmly packed
½   teaspoon ground cinnamon
⅛   teaspoon ground nutmeg
⅛   teaspoon ground ginger
¼   cup butter (4 tablespoons)

Combine the first five ingredients in a mixing bowl. Cut in the butter, using a pastry blender or crisscrossing with two knives, until the mixture is mealy in appearance.

Molasses Mixture:

½   teaspoon baking soda
¾   cup hot water
¾   cup light, mild-flavored molasses

Dissolve soda in hot water. Add molasses. Spoon one third of the molasses mixture into the pie shell. Cover with one third of the crumb mixture. Repeat this process twice. Bake the pie at 425 degrees for 10 minutes, then at 350 degrees 30 minutes longer. (Some of the molasses mixture may run over during baking. Put a large flat pan or a sheet of aluminum foil on the shelf below to catch any drippings.)

Serve slightly warm or cool, with whipped cream or vanilla ice cream if desired.

THE SOUTH

FROM THE PLANTATION cookery of Tidewater Virginia to the Creole specialties of New Orleans, the South is not *one* region but rather a collection of regions. Fried chicken only begins to tell the story of Southern cooking. There is the delicate rice and shrimp cookery of South Carolina, the pungent ham 'n' red-eye gravy of Tennessee, the catfish and hush puppies of inland Georgia, Alabama, and Mississippi.

Like all regional cookery, that of the South stems from the combined influences of the land and its people. What is the land of the South like? It is many things—bayous and cypress swamps, the rolling green-and-gold hills of the Piedmont country, the everlasting blue haze of the Southern highlands.

The coastal plain with its flat, often boggy country runs the curve of the Atlantic seaboard from Virginia southward and then travels westward along the shore of the Gulf of Mexico. All of Florida falls within the coastal plain, and no point within the state rises much more than 300 feet above sea level. In Virginia the coastal plain area is known as the Tidewater; in South Carolina, the Low Country.

Farther inland, paralleling the coastal plain, lies the gentle hilly countryside known as the Piedmont. And in the western sections of Virginia and North Carolina are the mountains themselves, the Southern Appalachians.

In Virginia this range is known as the Blue Ridge; in North Carolina, the Great Smokies. The highest mountain

peak east of the Mississippi is found in western North Carolina: Mount Mitchell reaching to a height of 6,684 feet and
outdistancing New Hampshire's Mount Washington by
nearly 400 feet. Beyond these peaks lies the Cumberland
Plateau, sloping westward across Kentucky and Tennessee to
the muddy Mississippi River plain.

**FOODS OF THE
SOUTHERN INDIANS**

The great Indian family of the southeast was the Muskhogean. Like the Iroquois and the Algonquians who domi-
nated large portions of the northeast, the Muskhogeans were
an agricultural people who added to their basic diet of corn,
beans, pumpkin, and squash whatever game or fish was available to them.

Some of the better-known tribes of the Muskhogean family
were the Choctaw, Chickasaw, Creek, Natchez, and Seminole.
They occupied the true heartland of the South—Georgia,
Alabama, Mississippi, and parts of Tennessee and Louisiana.
The Seminole, who live today in the Florida Everglades, did
not come to occupy this steamy swamp country out of choice.
Their original home was in southern Georgia and northern
Florida, and it was only after the persecution of the white
man made their lives unbearable that they fled to the
swamps.

The Muskhogean family, however, did not hold all of the
South. The Cherokee, an isolated but powerful tribe of the
Iroquois family, dwelt in parts of the interior. Like the Seminole, they were forced to flee their lands after the coming
of the white man. The fugitive Cherokee hid in the mountains of North Carolina, and their remnants can be found
there today, living on the Qualla Boundary Cherokee Indian
Reservation at the gateway to Great Smoky Mountains
National Park.

In eastern Virginia the Powhatan, a tribe of the Algonquian family, occupied the coastal region and were the first
to meet the Jamestown settlers. Their chief, also named Powhatan, was the father of Pocahontas.

Regardless of family or tribe, the southern Indians all ate much the same foods. Corn, as elsewhere in the East, was the staple, providing the Indian villages with corn bread and hominy, often referred to as lye-hominy. Because lye is a dangerous poison, its use in the preparation of food seems horrifying. However, the Indians had mastered a method of cooking dried corn kernels with lye water to make the hulls slip off. The whole tender hearts remaining were known as hominy.

The lye was extracted from wood ashes by a process known as leaching, or filtering water through the ashes. The poisonous effects of the lye were removed by giving the hominy several washings. It could then be cooked with chunks of meat or vegetables, or simply be boiled and eaten with bear grease or other fat. Whole hominy hearts are sometimes referred to as big hominy, while small hominy refers to hominy grits (grated or ground hominy).

Grits, served with eggs and country ham, is a standard breakfast dish in the South to this day. Hominy is usually prepared from white corn rather than the yellow corn that was so prevalent in the North. However, Indian hominy was likely to be red, orange, or even purplish-gray, depending on the brightly colored or speckled ears that were used in its preparation. The name hominy is derived from the Algonquian Indian word, *rockahominie*.

The warm southern climate with its long growing season permitted the Indians to cultivate crops, like sweet potatoes and melons, that were not so easily grown in the North. Tobacco was the important nonedible crop, grown by practically all the Indians of the South. Oil was obtained from the seeds of the sunflower, which the Indians cultivated, and from the kernels of the hickory, pecan, and other nuts which grew wild.

Wild fruits and berries, particularly strawberries and blackberries, were abundant throughout the South. The scuppernong was a native variety of yellowish-green grape with a plumlike flavor that grew along the shores of the Scuppernong River in North Carolina. Unlike other grapes, which grow in clusters, each fruit of the golden, spicy scup-

pernong hangs by its own individual stem. The colonists were to learn of these unusual grapes from the Indians, and scuppernong jams, jellies, brandies, and wines were to become popular regional specialties. The persimmon was another native fruit available to the Indians of the South. This small red-orange fruit has an astringent quality when not fully ripe. One bite seems to wrinkle the entire lining of the mouth. But if the persimmon is left to ripen until frost, its almost unbearable puckeriness disappears as if by magic, and the flesh becomes rich-tasting and sweetly mellow. Tennesseeans and other settlers used the pulp of the persimmon in cakes and breads.

Almost all of the game animals of the Northeast woodland Indians were also hunted by their neighbors to the south—bear, deer, squirrel, rabbit, raccoon. The opossum, however, was native almost exclusively to the southland. The Virginia opossum was especially prized by the Indians for its fattiness and tasty white flesh. This small animal, a little larger than a cat, but with a piglike snout and long hairless tail, is related to the kangaroo in that the female has an external pouch in which to carry her young. The opossum's habit of pretending to be dead in times of danger has given rise to the expression, "playing possum."

The opossum was hunted by the Indians chiefly during the autumn and winter months, for at these seasons the animals had a thick layer of fat under their skins. The colonists were to learn to cook and eat opossum from the Indians. Opossum is most often baked whole, accompanied by sweet potatoes, a dish lovingly known in the South as possum 'n' taters.

The peccary, or wild pig, was another animal that the Indians of the South used for food. Peccaries frequented cane thickets and swamps, particularly in what is now Arkansas and Louisiana, and lived on vegetable matter as well as rattlesnakes and water moccasins. They were known as musk hogs because of a gland located near the rump that contained a musky foul-smelling oil. The Indians learned to cut away this sac with care as soon as they had killed the peccary, in order to prevent contamination of the flesh. Even so, the meat of the peccary was vastly inferior to that of the domesticated hogs we know today.

Wild turkey, grouse, quail, ducks, and geese were also food for the Indians. In times when game was difficult to obtain, the Indians of the South, like their brothers elsewhere throughout the land, killed and ate fat dogs.

The Indians living near the bays and inlets of the ocean shore had crabs, clams, oysters, and in the brackish salt marshes they trapped the now rare diamondback terrapin. In the inland ponds and bayous there were snapping turtles and edible frogs to be had for the taking, and the rivers of the South were a source of bass, trout, catfish, bream, and crawfish, sometimes known as river shrimp.

These then were the native foods of this fertile sector of the New World. Many more were added by the colonists, and from this wealth of nature's produce sprang the rich and varied cookery of the American South.

FLORIDA COOKERY AND THE SPANISH

Forty-two years before the English landed in Virginia, the Spanish had established St. Augustine in Florida. This first permanent settlement of the white man in what is now the United States was founded in 1565. It was named for Augustine, the saint on whose day (August 28) land was sighted by the expedition.

Although St. Augustine was intended as a fort, built to assert Spain's claim to Florida and to protect Spanish shipping in the Caribbean, it served to introduce many Spanish imports of fruits, vegetables, and livestock into North America.

A typical dish of early Spanish days in St. Augustine was *garbanzo* soup. This soup was prepared with dried chickpeas, one of the world's oldest known legumes, plus other vegetables. *Chorizo,* a Spanish sausage, was added to the soup as was a pinch of saffron, a flavoring and coloring substance prepared from the yellow-orange stigmas of the crocus flower.

Ponce de León gave Florida its name when he landed on its shores on Easter Sunday in 1513. The Spanish words for this day are *Pascua florida* (flowery Easter). Fruits, as well as flowers, were destined to flourish in Florida. Orange trees were planted by the Spanish settlers during the 1500s, and grapefruit and lemon trees were introduced later, also by the Spanish.

The tiny wild limes that are native to the Florida Keys, in the southernmost reaches of the state, gave their name to Florida's key lime pie. The filling of this pie is a delicate and fluffy concoction of lime juice, sugar, and eggs. In more recent times, the Persian lime has been introduced into the Florida citrus belt. These limes are the size of lemons, green-fleshed and seedless, and they too make excellent lime pie.

Fish taken from Florida waters are noted for their rich and delicate meat. Especially delicious are red snapper, pompano, and mullet. Florida mullet is not to be confused with the East coast mullet of the northern states, which is a poor food fish. Great sea turtles caught off the Florida Keys are the basis of excellent turtle steaks that taste much like veal, while tiny periwinkle clams dug on Florida beaches at ebb tide make a tasty broth known as coquina soup.

The site of Jamestown is today a commemorative park, an unpeopled stretch of land beside the calm and almost color-less waters of the James River. In May of 1607 when the first English settlers arrived, tying their ships to the trees along the shore, this river must have looked much as it does now. For its placid surface reveals nothing of the bickerings and power struggles, the mutinies and executions, the town burnings, the sickness and starvation that took place along its banks during the early years in Virginia.

Nor does the river today reveal anything of its reign as

FROM THE "STARVING TIME" TO VIRGINIA TIDEWATER COOKERY

the plantation highway of the Tidewater, a period when ships arrived every week from afar to load tobacco at the private docks of the Virginia manor houses built along the James.

The tough, adventurous men who arrived at Jamestown under Captain John Smith fully expected to find both gold and silver in Virginia. Like many other Europeans they erroneously believed that North America was as rich a source of precious metals as South America had proved to be for the Spanish. Indeed so certain were they of achieving their goal that in their land contract they had agreed that one fifth of the gold and silver obtained in the New World would go to the British Crown. Needless to say, neither the Crown nor the colonists ever saw a grain of either metal from Virginia.

With little thought to the settlement of a colony, and no women along to attend to the finer domestic details, the Jamestown adventurers arrived low in provisions, and the ships that brought them almost immediately turned back for England to obtain additional supplies.

Once ashore, the men discovered they had so little food that their daily ration was a small amount of wheat and barley, all of it infested with worms and cockroaches from the long weeks of storage in the ship's hold. The Indians were generally hostile and were only occasionally willing to bring food to trade with the newcomers. When the Indians did trade, they very often exacted valuable items like powder and shot in return.

The Jamestown men were little skilled in hunting or fishing and spent a great deal of time panning the streams and washing the sands of the river bed for gold. No sooner had the ships returned from England, and the settlers laid in new stores of food and supplies, than fire broke out and the entire Jamestown settlement burned to the ground. So misfortune piled upon misfortune.

In 1609 the first women arrived at Jamestown, becoming wives for the men. But in that same year John Smith, who had been seriously wounded in an attempt on his life, was forced to return to England. Without Smith, the leader and the true provider of the colony, the period known as the

"starving time" set in. The colonists, who had already been reduced to eating snakes, now began to engage in the hideous practice of cannibalism. By 1610, with nine tenths of their number dead of starvation or sickness and with morale at an indescribable low, the remaining settlers decided to abandon Jamestown. The colony might well have disappeared (as had Sir Walter Raleigh's colony of 1585 on Roanoke Island in North Carolina) but for the timely arrival of a relief fleet under Lord De La Warr, newly appointed governor of Virginia.

The years that followed saw the successful experimentation with the tobacco plant by John Rolfe. After the dream of finding gold had collapsed, attempts had been made to build an economy for Virginia. Glass blowing, wine making, and silk culture had all been tried, and failed. Only lumbering had been partially successful.

Now Rolfe, taking his cue from the tobacco culture of the local Indians, tried planting some West Indian tobacco seed in the rich Virginia soil. The resulting leaf was superior to the "sotweed" of the Indians and was soon in demand in England. Little by little the Jamestown tobacco patches began to stretch out along the banks of the James. Land was available, but additional manpower to tend the fields was clearly needed. When in 1619 a Dutch ship sailed into the harbor at Jamestown with a cargo of Negroes, the tobacco-plantation economy of the South (and with it, Negro slavery) was born.

Many of the great plantation houses of colonial Virginia have been preserved or restored and may be visited today. High-ceilinged, with large airy rooms and a broad center hall running front to rear, these homes almost invariably had a separate kitchen building. No food was cooked in the main house itself. Sometimes a covered walk ran from the kitchen building to the "great" house, where the food was kept hot before the fireplace in the warming room, a kind of serving pantry just off the dining room. Most often, great covered dishes served to keep the food hot and free of insects and the elements as it was borne to the main house by Negro servants.

In addition to the kitchen building, the plantation had an assortment of other outbuildings—stables, blacksmith shop, carriage house, carpentry shop, laundry, smokehouse, dairy, and quite often an icehouse. Behind the plantation outbuildings lay the fields and the slave quarters. A broad sweep of lawn fronted the great house, displaying its grandeur from the river bank and the private dock below.

An enormous amount of slave labor was required to furnish such lavish rural living as the Virginia planters enjoyed in an unmechanized age. The icehouse, for example, took much human toil in both its construction and maintenance.

Icehouses were generally built near the river bank and were reached by means of an underground passageway. Ice was cut from the nearby ponds in wintertime or was received from New England by ship. It was then hauled by slaves, often crouched on all fours, through the narrow underground corridor to the icehouse itself, a sort of large cave braced with logs. Layers of straw separated the blocks of ice to facilitate their removal when needed.

On the larger estates, there were icehouses where up to twenty tons of ice could be stored. Thus the plantation

owner's family and guests were provided with iced drinks, ice cream, and other frozen desserts all through the long Southern summer.

The dairy was often referred to as the springhouse, for it was usually built directly over a flowing spring. Here great crocks of butter, milk, and cream were kept fresh and sweet as they stood "knee-deep" in the cold rippling water.

The smokehouse was the place in which the hams were hung after first being soaked in a brine solution or well rubbed with salt, pepper, and sugar. From hooks in the ceiling the hams were suspended over a smoke-producing fire of green logs. Hickory chips were often added for fragrance and flavor. Corncobs, too, were burned. Slow curing (salting and smoking) produced the highly flavored and long-keeping hams known as "country" hams that are still available throughout the South. The famous Smithfield hams were developed later, after it was discovered that hogs allowed to roam the countryside eating the peanuts that grew in the fields produced meat of superior flavor.

The peanut was native to South America, and like so many other vegetables (for the peanut is not a nut, but a member of the pea family), it came to North America via Europe and Africa. It was finally introduced into the American colonies during the 1600s by way of the African slave trade and was cultivated largely in Virginia until the Civil War. After that it spread to other parts of the South. Peanuts are also called groundnuts because they are the nut-like seed of a pod that is dug up from beneath the ground. In the South they are also commonly known as goobers, or goober peas, the word having been derived by Negro slaves from the African Bantu word for peanut, which was *nguba*.

As the hogs imported from England multiplied and the Virginia peanut fields expanded, more and more hogs began to thrive on peanuts, and a special curing and aging process was developed to bring out the rich flavor of the hams. The town of Smithfield in the heart of the Virginia peanut-growing and hog-raising belt became headquarters for the ham that bears its name. Today no ham may be labeled Smithfield unless cured within the corporate limits of that town.

The kitchen building of the Virginia plantation was one of the largest among the outbuildings. Sometimes it was the original dwelling house of a planter who had prospered and built a larger house, leaving the old one standing for conversion into a kitchen building. This took little doing for the main requirement was the fireplace which the original cabin was sure to have.

These fireplaces were often 6 feet high and as wide as 10 feet across. Both clay for making bricks and lime for the mortar were plentiful in the Tidewater. Chesapeake Bay oyster shells were an excellent source of lime. Kilns for baking bricks were in operation in the South in very early colonial times, permitting the construction not only of great fireplaces and tall chimneys but also of entire homes of lavish proportions built completely of brick.

The plantation kitchen fireplace was equipped with an iron lug pole, swinging cranes, and a good assortment of iron and copper cooking vessels, as well as other utensils. From the rafters hung drying vegetables and pot herbs taken from the kitchen garden. Flour, meal, and other staples were stored in the dry warmth of the kitchen building. Because of the size of both the fireplace and the kitchen staff, more than one complex or time-demanding dish could be prepared at once. Thus the turbaned slave Negress who was busy attending the kettles of frying chicken and stirring the cream gravy, did not have to be the same one who stood at the large center table giving five hundred whacks to the beaten biscuit.

Beaten biscuit was only one of the delicious hot breads that have made Southern cooking famous. To achieve just the right texture and lightness, the dough for these biscuits had to be beaten hard for at least half an hour. The purpose of this beating was to incorporate air into the mixture, for this was a time in history before the invention of baking powder, a chemical agent that liberates a gas, causing a cake or quick bread to rise during baking.

Traditionally the dough was placed on the smooth, flat surface of a tree stump and beaten with an iron pestle, a flatiron, or the side of a hatchet until it began to blister. Wooden boards called "biscuit blocks" were also used as a beating surface. It was said that if the biscuits were intended for everyday eating, three hundred whacks were sufficient— but if company were coming to dinner, no less than five hundred would do!

When the dough was smooth, satiny, and well blistered (indicating the presence of air), it was rolled out half an inch thick and cut into rounds with a biscuit cutter. The tops of the biscuits were pricked with a fork, and the biscuits were baked until they were a pale beige. They were always brought to the table hot and served with ham or chicken and lots of gravy.

Nowadays beaten biscuit may be made easily by running the dough through a meat grinder, but it is doubtful that this delicious hot bread would have existed at all had it not been for the kitchen slaves of the plantation South.

Sally Lunn was another favorite Virginia hot bread. It was named after an English girl who went through the streets of Bath selling her hot homemade buns. These delicate, fairly rich buns made with yeast, eggs, milk, flour, and a little sugar and butter were so well liked that the colonists brought the recipe along with them to Virginia. By this time the buns had become a bread baked in a shallow pan, cut into wedges or squares, and served hot with butter.

While both beaten biscuit and Sally Lunn had to be made with wheat flour imported from England, or exchanged in trade with the Middle Atlantic colonies, corn meal was the basis of most Southern hot breads. Southern corn bread was made with the local white corn meal and was usually baked in a shallow pan and cut in squares. It was always served hot. No sugar was used in Southern corn bread, in sharp contrast to the Northern variety, which included sugar and was generally made with yellow corn meal.

Hoecake, ashcake, and corn pone were all versions of Southern corn bread, baked as individual cakes. They were usually eaten by slaves or poorer farm families. Hoecake was made from a stiff batter of corn meal, milk or water, salt, and pork drippings or other fat. The dough was shaped into flat cakes, placed on a farm hand's hoe, and baked at an open fire for midday dinner out in the fields. Ashcake or ash bread was much the same thing except that it was baked directly in the hot ashes of the fireplace or open fire. It was sometimes wrapped in cabbage leaves to keep the gritty ash from coating the bread. Corn pone was any irregularly shaped lump of stiff batter baked in an oven or cooked like dumplings in boiling "pot likker" (the water, or liquor, in which ham or salt pork and greens had been cooked).

A much richer hot bread made with corn meal, milk, butter, and lots of eggs was spoon bread. It was served directly from the deep baking dish or pudding dish in which it was baked, the top and the sides fragrant and crusty, and the center soft and tender. Irregularly shaped pieces were dug out of the baking dish with a spoon and spread with melting butter.

Spoon bread is said to have originated as *suppawn,* the corn-meal-and-water porridge eaten by the New Netherland Dutch and many other colonists. Legend has it that an earthenware crock of *suppawn* was left too long on the fire to cook. By the time the forgetful housewife remembered it, it was no longer a porridge but had become crisp at the edges, although the center still remained creamy. It was eaten with butter and pronounced a masterpiece. Later eggs and milk were added for richer flavor, and spoon bread (known in a slightly different version as Virginia batter bread) was born. Spoon bread is often served with sugar-glazed ham and greens that have been simmered in salt-pork drippings.

As game was killed off, or retreated to the back country, more beef cattle, hogs, and poultry from abroad were imported into the Tidewater. Hog killing was a busy time, usually taking place just after the onset of cooler weather in fall so that the kill would keep longer. But, as always, most meat had to be salted or smoked, or both, in order to preserve it. The hams (thighs), shoulders, and sides of bacon were soaked in brine to ready them for the smokehouse where, with proper curing, they would keep for a year or even several years despite the long periods of hot weather in the South.

The back meat was usually chopped for sausage. Fresh sausage had to be highly seasoned with sage, pepper, and other spices to keep it from spoiling and also to disguise the off-flavors that developed when it did begin to "turn." Heads, feet, ears, and other odd parts were chopped up, cooked, and mixed with vinegar and spices for cooked sausages like souse and head cheese. Scrapple, too, was made in the South, using cooked meat scraps, pork livers, and corn meal.

The small intestines of the hog, known as chitterlings, were usually given to the slaves to eat. The favored method of preparation was to clean the intestines well and cook them in boiling water with a few spices until tender. Then the chitterlings were cut up into pieces about the size of an oyster, dipped in meal, and fried in deep hot lard until golden brown. "Chitlins" are still sold in most Southern butcher shops.

Hog jowl, the cheek or jaw of the hog, was also given to the slaves. It was generally cooked with black-eyed peas or with turnip greens. The hog fat was rendered, or melted down, into lard. The bits of skin that floated to the top of the lard kettle were the cracklings. Crisp fried cracklings were added to corn-bread batter to make a flavorful treat known as cracklin' bread.

Shortnin' bread, on the other hand, was really the "cake" of the poor South, beloved by "Mammy's little baby" and the children of many a humble farm family. It was a luxury food because it was made with wheat flour rather than the everyday corn meal, and included brown sugar for sweetening and butter or other shortening for richness. The ingredients were worked into a dough and patted into half-inch-thick rounds or other shapes, then baked.

In addition to the breads, pork, greens, and black-eyed peas that have been mentioned, the slaves of the Virginia tobacco plantations were given such cheap and plentiful foods as sweet potatoes, hominy grits, molasses, salt fish (received in trade with New England), and fresh beef parts when a kill had taken place. Small game such as opossum, squirrel, and rabbit helped to round out the slave diet.

A regional dish even more famous than possum 'n' taters was Brunswick stew. This stew originated in Brunswick County in southeastern Virginia. It was at first made with squirrel and no vegetables but onions. Later chicken was added, also fresh lima beans, green corn, okra and, even later, tomatoes. (Now chicken, or even veal and beef are likely to be included, while squirrel may be left out altogether.) Brunswick stew is a popular dish to this day, cooked in great steaming kettles and served at outdoor religious or political gatherings.

In contrast to the meals eaten by the slaves and by the families of the poorer Southern planters, the dinner tables of the great houses of Virginia glowed with wine jellies, cus-

tards, and brandied preserved fruits known as tutti-frutti. Other rich desserts, their recipes imported directly from England as were many of their ingredients, were plum pudding and trifle. Plum pudding was a steamed pudding made with raisins, currants, citron, spices, and brandy. Oddly enough it contained no plums. The word *plum* was used in the English sense, denoting a "choice bit," in this case the raisins, which like other preserved fruits were at one time a rarity and consequently a great delicacy.

Trifle was another typically English dessert, a concoction of cake slices soaked with rum or sherry, jam, and custard, all layered into a deep pudding dish. Because of its alcoholic content, trifle was also referred to as tipsy parson or tipsy squire.

George Washington cake, named for the master of Mount Vernon, was a very large fruitcake made with dried fruits, spices, and brandy. Such cakes were known in Virginia as "great cakes." Iced with a hard white sugar frosting, these cakes kept well for a long time.

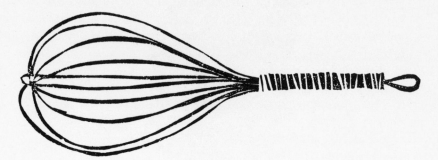

Probably the most famous of all Tidewater cakes, however, was Virginia poundcake, taken from an old English recipe. It was made with a pound each of butter, sugar, eggs, and flour (hence its name) and was flavored with brandy and mace. Since poundcake was originally made in the days before the invention of baking powder, the air had to be incorporated into the batter by beating. At least an hour of continuous beating was required for poundcake, and one recipe directed that the eggs be beaten for *five* hours before putting the batter to bake. Virginia poundcake, moist, high, and tender, reached its peak of perfection at the hands of the Negro slave women of the Tidewater plantations.

Chess pies, another Virginia favorite of English origin, were baked in small individual pie shells as tarts. The pie filling was a mixture of butter, sugar, eggs, raisins, and nut meats. Chopped dates were sometimes added. Fruit and custard-filled pies were also popular, but the truly American pie of the southland was sweet-potato pie.

To prepare the filling, the "sweets" were cooked, peeled, and mashed, then blended with sugar, eggs, lemon, and cinnamon. Sweet-potato pie was to the South what pumpkin pie was to New England. Milder in flavor and somewhat richer than pumpkin, it is truly a regional creation, a meeting of English pie pastry and the native American sweet potato that could have taken place nowhere but in the American South.

Beer was brewed from corn in the South, and was a popular morning drink, taken upon rising by the wealthy plantation folk as well as the poorer classes. Cider was less plentiful than in New England or the Middle Colonies because fewer apple trees had been planted, but peach brandies and blackberry cordials were distilled from the local fruits. Because tobacco was such a powerful item in trade abroad, wines including sherry and Madeira from Spain and Portugal were liberally imported into the South. Rum was also imported, but because of its harsh quality was not considered a gentleman's drink.

At Christmas and New Year's, rich eggnogs of cream, sugar, eggs, and brandy or sherry, sprinkled with nutmeg, were proffered to guests. Syllabub was an English recipe, a milk-and-wine punch very well liked in colonial times. It was made with cream, sugar, wine (usually sherry or Madeira), and lemon for flavoring. Syllabub was supposed to be served with a foamy topping, and the English aristocracy were said to have gone to great lengths to achieve this effect. In one fashionable London drawing room, both the cow and the milkmaid were led in before the assembled company and the milk squirted directly into the syllabub mixture to give it the desired froth. The syllabub was then passed to the guests, who ate the fluff off the top with a spoon and then drank the remainder of the potion, as was the custom. Although the colonists partook of a great deal of syllabub, no record exists of this direct milking practice being carried out in Virginia.

CHARLESTON AND THE CAROLINA RICE PLANTATIONS

Just as tobacco had become the gold of Virginia, rice was to become the chief source of wealth of the Carolina planters.

The territory of Carolina was a land grant made by the English crown. It included the present states of North Carolina, South Carolina, and part of Georgia. The English explored the area in 1663. Finding fertile soil and a warm climate, they were soon followed by the first settlers, who

brought quantities of seeds, slips, and roots, ready for planting grain, English garden vegetables, and fruits. It was also
hoped that the colonists would eventually be able to supply
England with wines, raisins, currants, oranges, lemons, olives,
and other items that she was then purchasing from Spain.
This dream was not to be realized.

By 1670, however, Charles Town (later Charleston) was
founded on the coast of what is now South Carolina. Because
of its splendid natural harbor, Charles Town was to remain
for many years the principal seaport and trading center of
the South, as well as the hub of a glittering social life.

No other city rose to challenge its position. In North
Carolina the coastal waters were dangerous, good harbors
were few, and piracy throve. In Virginia the plantations operated as small villages in themselves, and few people took up
life in the towns. Even Williamsburg, which became the
capital of Virginia in 1699 after the final burning of Jamestown, was a seat of government rather than a residential city.

It is doubtful, though, that Charles Town would have
achieved the prominence it did if not for a storm-damaged
ship that took refuge in its harbor sometime around 1680.
It is said that after the vessel had been repaired and was
about to depart its captain presented the governor of the
colony with a sack of Madagascar seed rice, a variety that
flourished from its very first planting in the Carolina Low
Country.

Like tobacco, the growing of rice demanded manpower as
well as suitable soil and climate. Since lowland rice must
grow most of its life standing in water, working conditions
in the rice fields of the hot, humid coastal region were close
to intolerable. Many of the marshy plains were malaria-
infested. White indentured servants, who worked for a master for a given time to pay off the cost of their passage to
America, refused to work in the rice fields. Negro slaves
were the answer, and a plantation system much like that
existing in Virginia and Maryland soon developed.

The Carolina plantations, however, were smaller and closer
together than those of Virginia and Maryland. Because of
the soggy rice lands surrounding the plantation houses many

wealthy Carolina planters kept handsome well-staffed town houses in Charleston which they visited often, especially in summer, to escape the unhealthful conditions of the rice country.

Later, in the 1740s, another crop became important in Carolina. This was indigo, a plant from which a much-in-demand blue dye was obtained. Although the production of indigo dye was a messy and unpleasant business requiring vats and tanks that bred flies and mosquitoes, slave labor made cultivation of the indigo plant profitable. The export of indigo to world markets brought even greater wealth to Charleston. At the same time, it increased the population and social life of the city, as the indigo planters joined the rice planters in building graceful galleried town houses surrounded by magnificent walled gardens.

Crabs and shrimp were abundant in the inlets and creeks of the Carolina coast. "She-crabs" were preferred to "he-crabs" for Charleston crab soup because the eggs of the "she-crab" added special flavor to the soup. If only "he-crabs" were available, Charlestonians added crumbled hard-cooked egg yolk to the soup. Charleston crab soup was not a humble dish. It had a milk base and, in addition to the eggs and lumps of crab, was enriched with sherry and garnished with whipped cream.

"Swimpee-raw!" as the street vendors of Charleston called it was the basis of numerous shrimp dishes including a shrimp paste that was served at breakfast time in South Carolina. The paste was a mixture of very finely ground cooked shrimp, butter, and seasonings. It was generally eaten cold, sliced, and accompanied by hot buttered hominy grits. Whole shrimp sautéed in butter was also a popular breakfast dish.

Shrimp and rice combinations were extremely popular. For shrimp and rice croquettes, finely chopped shrimp was mixed with cooked rice and beaten egg, rolled into cones, balls, or other shapes, dipped in crumbs, and fried golden brown and crusty in deep hot fat. These croquettes were the Southern counterpart of New England codfish balls, the rice and shrimp taking the place of the mashed potatoes and salt cod.

Shrimp pilau was a stewlike dish of rice and shrimp with onions. Later on, tomatoes were added. The word *pilau* (sometimes *pilaf*) comes from the Turkish and Persian and refers to a Near Eastern dish of cooked rice and other ingredients. Pilau traveled westward and reached America by way of the African slaves who were brought to her shores.

Rice was also simply served "plain boiled" with a lump of butter, but tender, flaky, and every grain separate. Or it might be molded into a rice ring and baked, or used in a Charleston corn bread known as philpy. Cooked rice was added to the batter, which was baked in a shallow pan, cut in wedges, and eaten warm with butter.

Awenda was another Carolina hot bread with an odd-sounding name. Believed to be of Indian origin, it was made with hominy grits, corn meal, milk, eggs, and butter—no flour. It was a custardlike version of spoon bread, and like all spoon breads was served directly from the baking dish and eaten hot, dripping with gravy or butter.

Carolina egg bread was still another type of spoon bread, but was made with more eggs. Because the eggs were separated and the whites beaten to a stiff froth before being added to the batter, Carolina egg bread rose high and puffy like a soufflé and had to be eaten very quickly lest it fall.

The African trade, in addition to its slave cargoes, brought many new foods to the American colonies. One of these was sesame seed, introduced to the Carolina colonists by their Negro slaves in the late 1600s. In the South sesame seeds are usually called benne seeds (*benne* being derived from the Malay word for "seed" or "grain"). Charleston benne wafers were a popular regional cooky made with brown sugar and lightly toasted sesame seeds. Another Charleston specialty was benne brittle, a "peanut" brittle candy without the peanuts. Toasted sesame seeds took their place.

A very famous South Carolina dessert was Lady Baltimore cake, which despite its name originated in the city of Charleston. "Lady Baltimore" was a beautiful and very queenly cake leavened with a great many beaten egg whites and flavored with essence of roses. It was filled and frosted with a white icing studded with chopped candied cherries, chopped figs, chopped pecans, and raisins—a cake as graceful and elegant as Charleston herself.

REGIONAL FOODS OF THE INLAND SOUTH

After the major coastal regions such as the Virginia Tidewater and the Carolina Low Country had been developed, many settlers began to drift westward across the South. Some of these were established colonists looking for new lands; others came directly from England or the Continent.

In Virginia the exhaustion of the soil in the tobacco lands sent many planters inland toward the Piedmont region. Tobacco was hard on the soil, and since no crop rotation was practiced it often left the land deprived and worthless after three years.

Land seeking and the adventurous spirit led Virginia explorers in 1670 to travel as far west as the Blue Ridge. From the crest of these mountains they looked beyond into what is now the state of West Virginia.

The first white settlers in this scenic hill country were Pennsylvania Germans who came in the early 1700s seeking farmlands. At about the same time, the Scotch-Irish appeared, a fiercely independent people who seemed ever drawn to the rough life of the frontier.

The Scotch-Irish were really Scotsmen who had been living for many years in Ireland, working chiefly as weavers of cloth. English laws which placed high tariffs on their goods made their lives difficult. When in 1714 religious persecution set in as well, the Scotch-Irish began to leave Ireland in droves. A great many settled in the hilly frontier country of the South—in Kentucky, Tennessee, and the western part of North Carolina, as well as in West Virginia.

Welsh and English settlers also took up lands in the western part of the Virginia territory before the Revolutionary War, but life beyond the Appalachians was very different from that in the tobacco-plantation country. Since the land was hilly and even mountainous in some areas, only small farm holdings were practical. The plantation system never developed, and staffs of Negro slaves were not required on the small hill farms.

It is not surprising, therefore, that at the time of the Civil War the western territory of Virginia opposed secession from the Union and in 1861 organized a separate government which became known as the state of West Virginia. The development of West Virginia's coal industry and other mineral resources after the Civil War was to draw Italian, German, Polish, and Hungarian immigrants.

Kentucky was also originally a part of the Virginia territory. In 1750 the discovery of a pass in the mountains now known as the Cumberland Gap gave the first explorers a glimpse of the rugged but beautiful country of eastern Kentucky. In 1769 Daniel Boone passed through the Gap with a hunting party and spent almost two years exploring the Kentucky wilderness. The first permanent white settlements were established in 1774 by colonists from Pennsylvania, Virginia, Maryland, North Carolina, and eastern Tennessee. Most were of English or German stock, and in many isolated mountain communities in both Kentucky and Tennessee the descendants of English settlers have preserved speech patterns, folklore, and old ballads that date back to Elizabethan times.

One of the earliest regional dishes of the Kentucky frontier was hunter's stew. There was no fixed recipe, of course. The stew consisted of choice bits of whatever freshly killed game was on hand—deer, elk, bear, wild turkey, or even buffalo. These were boiled in a kettle over an open fire with sage and red pepper, both commonly used in England.

The explorers of the frontier were known as long hunters. This name may have been applied by the settlers back home because of the hunters' long sojourn into the wilds, often for months at a time, to trap game for fur and hides, reconnoiter, and trade with the Indians. The name may also have been bestowed by the Indians because of the long rifles the hunters carried.

At the end of a long hunt supplies of corn meal were usually gone, and the hunters found themselves on a diet consisting almost exclusively of meat. Breast of turkey, because of its blandness and grainy texture, then became the long hunter's "bread." A roasted kidney or stewed bear's liver also served as "bread," offering some of the longed-for contrast in flavors and textures.

The pioneers coming into Kentucky brought supplies of corn meal, salt, smoked ham and bacon, and wheat flour if they had any, to tide them over the early days of settlement. Corn was planted as soon as possible, for it was the food of greatest basic importance. In addition to supplying meal for breads and porridge, hominy (both big and small), and green ears for roasting, corn was food for livestock, particularly the hogs that were a source of meat and lard. The Virginia settlers had brewed beer from corn, and on the Kentucky frontier whisky was distilled from corn. Bourbon, a corn whisky widely produced today, was first made in Bourbon County, Kentucky.

Wheat did not do well in the new soil which was apparently too rich in humus. When the soil had been reduced after two to three years of planting corn, some wheat was grown. But the delicate wheat shafts, with their exposed ears of grain, were prey to weeds, birds, and small animals. Corn was by far the hardier crop for the wilderness. Wheat flour, either home-grown or purchased (at three to four times the cost of corn meal), was reserved for special uses, perhaps for biscuits at Sunday morning breakfast, or for a pie crust or gingerbread.

Corn meal filled in the rest of the time—for mush, for hoecake, for corn pone, for cracklin' bread, and for corn dodger (which was baked in large flat rounds, sometimes in a pie pan, and was similar to New England johnnycake). Corn bread in one form or another was often served in the same meal as hominy or grits.

The settlers planted vegetables, particularly sweet pota-

toes, Irish potatoes, okra, and green beans. Green beans and
bacon was a favorite dish everywhere in the South and still
is. The green beans (also called snap beans and string beans)
were simmered very slowly with the bacon or other cured
hog meat nearly all day. By serving time the beans had
turned a washed-out gray, but their smoky flavor was delicious. Sometimes diced Irish potatoes, roasting ears cut up
into chunks, or okra pods were added to the dish making it
almost a vegetable stew.

Come spring, the frontier settlers began to gather wild
greens almost as soon as the first sprouts were above the
ground. Cooked with smoked ham hocks, hog jowl, or bacon,
or just in the "pot likker" from these cured meats, a "mess
o' greens" was a welcome treat after the long winter's diet of
only dried or root vegetables. Some of these "salat greens"
or "pot herbs," all of which were weeds, bore colorful names
such as lamb's quarters, plantain, and poke. Pokeweed in its
mature state produces poisonous leaves and berries, but its
first shoots in spring are harmless. It was said that in the
first season on the frontier the Kentucky women followed
the cows when they went greens-gathering, picking only the
plants the cows ate as a guarantee that they weren't poisonous.

Many of the settlers were of English origin and possessed the Englishman's love of meat. Since game was plentiful on the frontier, it was not unusual for meat to be served three times a day. Bear was a common food in the early days. Bear bacon and bear hams were smoked in the same manner as pork. The cubs especially were regarded as a delicacy, and wild turkeys were customarily larded with bear grease before roasting.

After bear and venison became scarce, pork was the most popular meat on the frontier, just as it was throughout most of the South. This was probably because pork could be preserved by smoking most successfully and most tastily. Salted beef was never as well liked in the South as it was in New England. In addition salt was scarce in the backwoods and therefore expensive. It was estimated that in the years before 1800 salt cost three to four times the price of the beef, and the general feeling was that salt beef wasn't worth it.

The frontier settlers thus arrived at a system whereby a man would divide his beef kill with all of his neighbors who lived within reasonable hauling distance. A short time later another neighbor who had just slaughtered a beef cattle would do the same. In this way fresh beef was available to all almost throughout the year, and the problem of meat spoilage was kept to a minimum.

Watermelons grew untended in the corn patch, and wild blackberries were to be had for the picking, but orchard fruits were little cultivated on the frontier. Wild honey was a much-used sweetener, for molasses from the West Indies was difficult to obtain during the Revolutionary War, and sugar, up from New Orleans, was expensive. Settlers who owned some "sugar bush" had maple sugar, produced from the sap of the sugar maple just as it was in New England.

Hot corn bread and butter were almost always eaten with honey. Honey, too, provided metheglin, an alcoholic beverage of English derivation, similar to the mead of old England. Since honey (unlike man-made sweeteners) does not ferment naturally, yeast had to be added to bring on the fermentation. Metheglin was only made, however, when honey was plentiful.

Cider was scarce because few apple trees were planted on the frontier, and the import of rum, chiefly from the West Indies, was cut off as molasses had been during the Revolution. Barley and the small grains from which beer was ordinarily brewed grew poorly in the new soil. These factors led to the increasing consumption of corn whisky and the equipping of many a frontier cabin with a still (distilling apparatus) for its production.

Corn whisky was often drunk at breakfast time along with a substantial meal that included eggs, grits, hoecake or corn bread with butter and honey, and several meats from a list that might include home-cured bacon, ham, fried beef, squirrel, chicken, sausage, and souse. Dinner was at midday or a little past and included almost everything served at breakfast plus sweet potatoes, cooked vegetables, and possibly cooked greens. Corn-meal mush served with milk was a common dish at supper, particularly for the children of the family. Many adults, however, had their third meat meal of the day at this time.

It was not at all unusual, on the frontier as elsewhere in the South, for freshly baked hot breads to be served at all three meals. Firewood was plentiful, and breads made with corn meal tasted much better hot than cold. The breads served in the frontier cabins, however, were simpler, with hoecake and plain corn bread the most common. The beaten biscuit and spoon bread of the plantation South were too costly of time, labor, and ingredients for the chore-laden frontier woman in her modest mountain cabin.

Burgoo is undoubtedly the most famous of all Kentucky regional dishes that have come down to us from the past. Burgoo is the stew served in Kentucky on Derby Day, as well as at political rallies, elections, and other sporting events and outdoor gatherings. It is very much the counterpart of Virginia's Brunswick stew and was originally prepared with squirrel or chicken, and vegetables. Modern burgoos are likely to include an almost endless list of vegetables: okra, corn, limas, peppers, tomatoes, cabbage, onions, celery, carrots, and potatoes. Squirrel is still used now and then. Chicken is always present, and lamb, pork, veal, and beef may be added as well, with red pepper as an important seasoning.

Burgoo is usually cooked outdoors in great iron kettles and is prepared over a period of several hours by special burgoo chefs. When the crowd to be served is very large, burgoo is generally dispensed in tin cups, and the quantities required of each ingredient become staggering. Thus recipes exist for burgoos that make 1,200 gallons! A burgoo is also the name given to an outdoor communal event in Kentucky, just as New England has its clambakes and the Southwest its barbecues.

Tennessee, which lies just south of Kentucky, was first explored by De Soto in 1541 and later, in 1673, by Marquette and Joliet. But despite both Spanish and French claims in the territory, the first permanent settlements were made about 1679 under the English flag. Most of the settlers were Scotch-Irish, English, or French Huguenot, and had come from Virginia and the Carolinas.

Because of Tennessee's great width (432 miles across), the state can be divided into three fairly distinct areas. Eastern Tennessee is hill country that takes in the Great Smoky Mountains, boasting a number of peaks over 6,000 feet. Middle Tennessee is largely a plains area, while western Tennessee is a Mississippi Valley lowlands. This last region with its cotton plantations and its Memphis slave market (established in the early 1800s) was to become very "deep South" in character.

The cookery in Tennessee has followed the terrain. In hilly eastern Tennessee the foods and regional cookery closely resembled those of Kentucky and other mountain frontier regions. Western Tennessee, on the other hand, developed a plantation tradition in cooking similar to that of the Virginia Tidewater and the Carolina Low Country.

While ham rivals fried chicken as the "national" dish of the South, Tennessee is particularly well known for its ham 'n' red-eye gravy. Home-cured country ham, unlike the tenderized pink packing-house ham of modern times, is highly salted, fairly hard and dry due to long smoking, and a deep mahogany in color. A fuzzy greenish mold often develops on the outside of the ham and, although harmless, it must be scrubbed off with a stiff brush before using.

Country ham, therefore, must first be soaked overnight and then very slowly cooked in simmering water. It may also be cut into not-too-thick slices and fried in a hot skillet. For red-eye gravy, the drippings from the pan in which the ham has been fried are blended with some water and a little black coffee. Then the pungent gravy is poured over the fried ham slice. Grits and lots of hot fluffy biscuits are served with this dish, for these bland foods are perfect in flavor contrast to the ham, and the biscuits are especially useful for mopping up the gravy.

Although Georgia has an Atlantic coastline of almost one hundred miles, the bulk of this state extends inland to the great heart of the South. Georgia, the largest state east of the Mississippi, was settled in 1733 by the English under James Oglethorpe as a home for jailed debtors and paupers. The real purpose of settlement, however, was to establish an English territory to act as a watchful check on the Spanish in Florida and to keep them from moving northward toward the colonies of the Carolinas and Virginia.

The English hoped not only to develop silkworm culture in Georgia but also to plant vineyards for a wine industry, but the country was not well suited to either of these ventures. Peaches and pecans were to become important in their stead.

The peach is thought to be a native of China, and like many other fruits it was introduced into North America by the Spanish in Florida in the 1500s. The peach tree grows easily from seed, and by the time the English settlers arrived, peach trees were growing wild in Georgia and had been flourishing, in fact, as far north as Virginia for some time.

Pecans, on the other hand, were native to the southerly reaches of the Mississippi River. Pecan trees spread from the state of Mississippi across Alabama to Georgia, and today these three states, as well as others including Texas, claim honors for pecan pie. The heated competition is understandable, for this rich, irresistible combination of butter, eggs, sugar, corn sirup, and pecan meats is surely worth fighting over. A swirl of whipped cream or a scoop of vanilla ice cream adds a superb crowning touch.

It is interesting to note that pecan pie was very much a product of the Mississippi River area of the South where cane sugar from Louisiana was readily available. Had pecan trees been native to, let us say, Massachusetts, we would have had a very different recipe for pecan pie than we do today, with molasses or possibly maple sugar the principal sweetener.

A popular regional chicken dish in Georgia is country captain, so named because it was believed to have originated with the captain of a spice-cargo ship that took harbor in Savannah, Georgia, in colonial days. The dish, which slowly drifted inland, carried with it a whiff of the Orient, for it was prepared with curry, rice, currants, almonds, and various spices.

A word ought to be said here, too, about Southern fried chicken. There are some differences of opinion throughout the South as to its manner of preparation, just as there are differences regarding the correct preparation of baked beans in New England.

The simplest method is to coat the chicken pieces before frying by shaking them in a paper bag together with some flour, salt, and pepper. But some Southern cooks dip the chicken pieces first into beaten egg and then into flour, corn meal, or bread crumbs—while others dip the chicken into a prepared batter of flour, eggs, and milk before frying. Whatever the method, almost all seem to agree on the merits of cream gravy, prepared by adding flour and thin cream to some of the fat in which the chicken has been fried. Seasoned with salt, pepper, and grated nutmeg and poured hot over crisp golden-fried chicken, cream gravy makes delectable eating anywhere in the gravy-loving South!

Both Alabama and Mississippi, which lie to the west of Georgia, were first explored by the Spanish and later by the French, who attempted colonization. The city of Mobile, Alabama, was founded in 1702 and became the first permanent white settlement in the state. Biloxi, Mississippi, was founded even earlier, in 1699. Despite their French background, the populations of both these states were swelled by Englishmen loyal to the crown at the outbreak of the American Revolution. Most of these British sympathizers were from the colonies of Virginia, the Carolinas, and Georgia, where they found themselves highly unpopular.

After the Revolution other planters came west, and spurred by the invention of the cotton gin in 1792, they established cotton plantations in Alabama and Mississippi. Slavery was widespread, and the plantation kitchens produced a rich and elegant cookery reminiscent of that of Virginia and South Carolina one hundred years earlier.

Fried pies are sometimes attributed to Alabama, but these crisp, delicate, half-moon pastries may be sampled in almost every Southern state. The fillings vary with the locality. In Virginia, fried pies are most likely to be filled with cooked sweetened apples or with thick applesauce. In Georgia or Alabama, peach butter (fresh sugared peaches cooked down to a thick jam) makes a luscious center; and in the mountain regions, wild blackberry jam is an old-fashioned favorite.

Whatever the fruit used, a small mound of filling is heaped onto a round of rolled-out pie crust. The pastry is then flipped over to make a half-moon, sealed at the edges, and fried quickly in deep fat. Fried pies are eaten hot, snowy with powdered sugar.

Mississippi is catfish country. In its rivers and in those of western Tennessee just to the north, bewhiskered monsters weighing from 30 to 100 pounds have been caught. Smaller catfish abound in fresh-water streams throughout the South, as do bass, trout, bream; and many other varieties. This wealth of sweet-fleshed, good-eating fish led from earliest times to the popular institution of the Southern fish fry.

At fishing camps or on casual outings along river banks the fresh-caught fish was rolled in corn meal and then fried, on the spot, in hot fat. Inseparable from fried fish was the hush puppy, a small lump of stiff batter consisting of corn meal, water or milk, and sometimes an egg, seasoned with onion, salt, and pepper. Fried to a crusty golden-brown in the same fat as the fish, the hush puppy is the perfect and most mouth-watering of accompaniments.

The story of how the hush puppy got its name probably goes back to the very first fish fry. As the hounds who had come along on the expedition caught the savory odor of the frying fish, they began to whine with unbearable-sounding pangs of hunger. It thus became customary for their masters to toss them some of the newly fried bits of corn meal with the soothing words, "Hush, puppy!"

Today in the South, hush puppies are traditional with fish, be it catfish in inland Georgia, or fried clams and other seafood in coastal North Carolina.

Arkansas, on the western shore of the Mississippi, is something of a border state combining the plantation cookery of its Mississippi Valley region, the hill cookery of the Ozarks, and also reflecting, on its Texas and Oklahoma boundary, the Mexican influences of Southwestern cookery. Explored by the Spanish in the 1500s and the French in the 1600s, Arkansas remained a sparsely inhabited region until the Louisiana Purchase in 1803. After that it was settled by pioneers of English and Scotch-Irish ancestry coming from Kentucky and Tennessee, and by cotton planters from the eastern shores of the Mississippi.

THE CREOLE COOKERY OF LOUISIANA Louisiana received somewhat more attention than its neighbor to the north from early French explorers, and in 1718 the city of New Orleans was founded. Between 1727 and 1751 France sent shiploads of "casket girls" to become brides in the new colony.

The casket girls were so named because the government provided each of them with a small chest containing articles of clothing and household apparel which were to serve as a trousseau or dowry to be presented to the men they were to marry. Nuns chaperoned the brides-to-be on the voyage from France.

The casket girls adjusted remarkably well to the raw city built on muddy ground and surrounded by swamps. Their first homes were huts built of clay held together with the Spanish moss that so liberally festooned the trees in the bayous and forests of Louisiana, as it did everywhere throughout the humid South. An outer framework of split boards or posts, cut from knobby-kneed swamp cypress, acted as a support. In areas where there was a great danger of flooding, the houses were frequently built on stilts of cypress logs and rose from six to eight feet above ground level.

The casket girls brought touches of French elegance to New Orleans, in their manner of dress, in the furnishings of their rude dwellings, and of course in their cookery. Their chief complaint was the corn meal of the New World, which seemed to them a poor substitute for the fine white wheat flour they had known in France.

From 1755 on, many Cajuns, French Canadians driven from Canada by the British, came to settle in Louisiana. The word *Cajun* was derived by slurring the sounds in the word *Acadian*, for these people were from the part of Canada once known as Acadia and now comprised chiefly of Nova Scotia. The industrious Cajuns, who were skilled spinners and weavers, brought still another kind of French influence to Louisiana.

Then in 1762 France ceded her Louisiana territory to Spain, bringing wealthy Spaniards to New Orleans. Along with them came the lacy iron grillwork and trellised balconies of Spanish architecture, and the spicier seasonings and piquant flavors of Spanish food. Despite Spanish ownership many French aristocrats fled to Louisiana during the French Revolution, taking with them their chefs and household staffs. In 1800 Spain returned Louisiana to France, and in 1803 the entire territory became part of the United States by means of the Louisiana Purchase.

The intermarriage of the French and Spanish settlers of Louisiana produced a people known as Creoles, and the mixture of the two cultures created Creole cookery. But other influences are also strongly seen in this unique cuisine. These are the contributions of the native Choctaw Indians, of the Negro slaves from Africa and the West Indies, and of the land and surrounding waters which provided such special foods as rice, sugar, pecans, shrimp, crabs, redfish, and pompano.

Negroes were brought to Louisiana from the earliest days of settlement. The planting of sugar cane, which the Spanish had introduced to the West Indies, was undertaken on a large scale in Louisiana around 1750. This brought additional numbers of Negro slaves who were to add their own culinary graces to the French and Spanish cookery at hand.

An important cooking ingredient bestowed by the Choctaw Indians was filé powder, made from the dried pulverized leaves of the sassafras plant. The Choctaws used filé powder medicinally, but the Negro cooks adapted it for use as a thickening agent in their superb gumbos, thick soups or stews served with rice.

Gumbo is also the name applied to the dialect spoken by the Negroes of Louisiana. And to cause further confusion gumbo is also another name for okra, a podlike vegetable native to Africa and brought to the New World, like the sesame seed, by way of the slave trade. Okra has a mucilaginous quality and is used, like filé powder, to thicken the stews known as gumbos.

Crab gumbo is among the most popular, but chicken, shrimp, ham, and oysters are used in gumbo, either alone or in combination. The vegetables used in a gumbo are usually onions, green peppers, tomatoes, and okra. In New Orleans the okra is often omitted, and just the filé powder is used for thickening. Filé powder must never be cooked, and is therefore added to the hot gumbo just before serving. Although rice is an important ingredient of gumbo, it is cooked separately. At serving time, a mound of hot rice is placed in a soup plate, and the gumbo is poured over it.

Crawfish, also called crayfish and sometimes "river shrimp," are fresh-water shellfish somewhat like miniature lobsters. Crawfish are delicious boiled like lobster or cooked in a Louisiana soup known as crawfish bisque.

Probably the most celebrated of all Louisiana fish soups is bouillabaisse. The Creole version of this renowned fish stew from the south of France is considered by some to be the best in the world because of the unsurpassable flavor of the fish caught in the Gulf of Mexico. Creole bouillabaisse is usually made with red snapper and redfish. The other ingredients are mushrooms, onions, garlic, tomato pulp, sherry or white wine, and seasonings. This chowder is usually served in a deep plate over slices of toasted French bread. The rather lengthy name for this dish is simply a combination of the French words meaning "boil" and "stop," indicating that the stew is to be very lightly cooked, for overcooking toughens fish.

Pompano, a superb delicate-meated fish caught in the Gulf and other southern waters, is often baked in little folded paper hearts to preserve its flavor and juices. Enclosed in each parchment paper case is an individual serving of pompano topped with a rich sauce of crawfish, crabmeat, and shrimp. This very elegant dish is known as *pompano en papillotes* and is served in choice New Orleans restaurants, reputed to be the finest in the country, particularly in their offerings of French and Creole dishes.

Pompano may also be baked Creole style with tomatoes, onions, green pepper, spices, and herbs. Red snapper Creole is also extremely popular along the Louisiana Gulf coast.

Edible frogs, considered a great delicacy, are plentiful in Louisiana, where they are often hunted in the bayous at night with a flashlight attached to a harpoon. Louisiana cooks prepare frog legs either by sautéing them in butter or breading them in corn meal or cracker crumbs and then frying them in deep fat. The meat is white, sweet and delicate, and strongly resembles chicken. Only the hind legs of the frog are eaten, and these must be skinned before cooking.

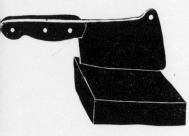

Jambalaya is a stew of rice and other ingredients which gets its colorful, melodious name from the French Provencal word, *jambalaia*. Many jambalayas are made with chopped or diced ham, but shrimp, chicken, crabmeat, oysters, and sausage are also used, alone or in combination, with the usual Creole vegetables, herbs and seasonings. The rice which is usually cooked *with* the jambalaya absorbs most of the liquid (broth, water, or tomato juice) so that no thickener is required. A jambalaya makes a delicious meal-in-a-dish, and its fame has rightly spread beyond the confines of the Creole country.

Rice was being grown in Louisiana and was even being exported to Europe during the early 1700s. It is not surprising, therefore, that the Louisiana version of the doughnut should be a deep-fried rice fritter. These puffy, golden-brown cakes are known as *calas*, and are prepared with cooked rice, eggs, sugar, flour, nutmeg or lemon rind, and vanilla flavoring. They are yeast-raised for lightness, or, in modern times, may be made with baking powder.

In the old days in New Orleans, Negro women sold hot *calas* on the streets of the French Quarter on Sunday mornings after church, calling out, *"Belle cala, tout chaud!"*— "beautiful *calas*, nice and hot." It was the custom for churchgoers to buy these little cakes from the vendors and take them home for breakfast, to be served with *café au lait* (coffee with hot milk, in equal proportions).

Morning Call, a custom prevalent to this day, is that of having coffee and delicate, thinly frosted French crullers, or *beignets* (round puffed French doughnuts) in one of the coffee shops in the old French Market. Here, too, in the late evening hours, New Orleans coffee lovers are again likely to convene.

Other rolls of French origin are also popular with coffee in New Orleans: *brioches* (very rich muffins baked in fluted and flared forms, each crowned with a glossy golden-brown topknot) and *croissants* (flaky, buttery crescent-shaped rolls).

Pain perdu is a thrifty way of reviving stale bread by dipping slices in a sweetened egg-and-milk mixture, frying in butter, and serving with jelly, honey, or sirup. *Pain perdu* (meaning "lost bread") is known all through the United States simply as French toast.

While *café au lait* is taken at most meals in New Orleans, a very spectacular after-dinner coffee is *café brûlot* (flaming coffee). For a most stunning effect, *café brûlot* is prepared before the assembled dinner guests in a darkened room. Brandy, orange and lemon peel, whole cloves, cinnamon sticks, and lump sugar are ignited in a silver or other heat-tolerant bowl. While these blaze, hot strong coffee is slowly poured into the bowl, and when the flames are quenched the spiced and pungent brew is ladled into demitasse or other small cups and passed. *Café brûlot* is always served black.

Pralines are the candy for which New Orleans is famous. They are named for a French butler, Praslin, who had almonds coated with sugar for his master, as a precaution against indigestion. The usefulness of this sweetmeat as a remedy is not known. In Louisiana, however, where the pecan grew wild and sugar cane was cultivated from early times, the delicious confection known as the pecan praline soon evolved. Pralines are large, flat patties made with brown sugar, water or cream, butter, and pecans, of course. They are firm, but have a velvety fudgelike texture that blends superbly with the rich flavor of the pecan meat. Like most old-fashioned candies, however, they are *very* sweet.

FESTIVALS AND HOLIDAYS OF THE SOUTH

From the Old English Christmases of the Virginia colony to the Mardi gras of present-day New Orleans, the South has always exhibited a love of light and carefree merrymaking. Each section of this richly varied region seems to have its own special form of festive expression.

In Virginia and South Carolina where the English influence was strongest, Christmas and New Year were celebrated with plum puddings and eggnogs in the tradition of the mother country, and many English holiday customs have lingered to the present. Festivities of a different sort are the mountain sings and handicrafts fairs that are an important feature of life in the highlands of North Carolina. Kentucky, of course, has its burgoos; there are fish fries in Georgia, Alabama, and Mississippi; and in Louisiana there is the Mardi gras.

Mardi gras (which is French for "fat Tuesday") is Shrove Tuesday, the day preceding Ash Wednesday, the first day of Lent. It is a day of merrymaking and carnival celebrated in a number of parishes, or counties, in Louisiana, in the French-founded Gulf city of Mobile, Alabama, and also in some cities in Florida. In New Orleans the parades of floats, the masquerading, the marching music makers, and the general revels all reach their climax in a grand ball before midnight, for this is the end of rich eating and gay living until after the forty days of fasting and penitence from Ash Wednesday to Easter.

One tradition that seems fairly widespread in the South is that of eating Hopping John on New Year's Day. "Eat peas on New Year's Day," the saying goes, "and you will have good luck for the rest of the year." Made with dried red peas, salt pork or bacon, rice, butter, and salt and pepper, Hopping John is eaten piping hot with buttered corn bread. For extra luck, Southern children sometimes hop around the table before sitting down to partake of this promising dish.

FOODS AND PEOPLE OF THE SOUTH TODAY

Although the South has developed many industries since the Civil War, she is still chiefly devoted to agriculture. For this reason not as many people from foreign lands have come to take up life and work in the South during the past century as have settled in New England and the Middle Atlantic States. The population of the South remains predominantly British (including the Scotch and Irish) and African Negro in origin.

The principal exception to this, of course, is the large French population of Louisiana, including the Cajuns from Canada. There are also some old French families in South Carolina. Germans are to be found in North Carolina and in the northern sections of Kentucky and West Virginia. Descendants of the original Spanish settlers still live in parts of Florida and Louisiana. Cuban and Greek fishermen live in communities along the Florida coast.

The food products of the South have not changed drastically over the years, but their yield has been dramatically increased, and their processing and marketing have been streamlined. In addition to its food crops, it must be remembered that a large portion of the acreage of the South is given over to the cultivation of cotton and tobacco.

Virginia is an important source of peanuts, apples, and corn. Poultry and hog raising are prominent activities, with the town of Smithfield a packing center for Smithfield and Virginia hams. Virginia's Chesapeake Bay waters yield oysters, crabs, and other shellfish.

North Carolina might well have been the site of the first permanent English settlement on North American shores had Sir Walter Raleigh's colony, established on Roanoke Island in 1585, survived. Virginia Dare, the first child of British parentage in America, was born here in 1587. But this happy event was followed by the total and mysterious disappearance of what is now referred to as "The Lost Colony." The first permanent settlements in North Carolina were made by Virginians of English, Scotch, and Irish descent about 1650. German and Swiss colonists settled the coastal town of New Bern in 1710, but difficult shore approaches kept this northern sector of the Carolina territory sparsely settled for many years. North Carolina was separated from South Carolina in 1729.

Like Virginia, North Carolina produces peanuts, apples, and corn. Sweet potatoes grow well here, as do peaches, strawberries, watermelons, and cantaloupes. Wilmington, a seaport on the North Carolina coast, sends oysters, crabs, clams, and other fish to market.

Rice, once the staple of South Carolina and the very basis of her economy, is no longer an important commercial

crop in this state. The heavy farm machinery now used for planting and harvesting rice was found to be impractical in the soft swampy ground of the Low Country. With the passing of slavery and hand labor in the rice fields, rice cultivation moved to Arkansas, Louisiana, and other parts of the South where the soil is artificially irrigated and can be dried firm at planting and harvesting time.

Other food crops have taken the place of rice in South Carolina—peaches, strawberries, and watermelons; pecans and peanuts; Irish and sweet potatoes. South Carolina has large seafood canneries and also markets fresh oysters, crabs, and shrimp.

West Virginia has been called the most northern of the Southern states, and the most southern of the Northern states. Although much of the state is given over to manufacturing and coal production, buckwheat, peaches, and apples are important food products. The Golden Delicious apple originated in West Virginia and is now known throughout the country for its mellow flavor and lovely pale waxen skin.

Kentucky produces corn, much of which goes into the distilling of its famous bourbon whisky. Sweet potatoes are grown in the western part of the state, and sorghums, a cane-like grass that produces sorghum sirup and sorghum molasses, are grown for local consumption. Hogs and poultry are raised, as they are almost everywhere in the South, and sheep graze in the celebrated Bluegrass country, where some of the finest horses in the United States are bred.

Tennessee raises beef and dairy cattle in its plainslike central region. Corn is a leading crop. Sorghums are grown for local use, and strawberries and watercress are attractive special items of produce.

Georgia, Alabama, and Mississippi share many popular agricultural products: peaches, watermelons, cantaloupes, sugar cane, sweet potatoes, corn, pecans, and peanuts. Apples are grown in the northern highlands of Georgia and Alabama.

Georgia, with its Atlantic seacoast, ships quantities of shrimp and crabmeat. The coastal city of Brunswick is an important processing center for breaded and frozen shrimp. The Gulf states of Alabama and Mississippi bring oysters and shrimp to market, as well as sea trout, Spanish mackerel, and redfish, for which the Gulf of Mexico is famous.

Florida has been called the "Orange State" for obvious reasons. Her yield of citrus fruits is remarkable in both quantity and scope—oranges, grapefruits, lemons, limes, tangerines, and the tiny orange-gold kumquats that may be eaten skin and all. Strawberries, watermelons, and peaches are also grown, as well as semitropical fruits like avocados, pineapples, and mangoes. Sweet corn, celery, and numerous other vegetables are important Florida products, as are peanuts and pecans. Beef and dairy cattle are raised in central Florida, and from her waters comes nearly half the nation's shrimp supply. Florida also sends to market clams, oysters, crawfish, and crabs (including the prized Florida stone crab), as well as scallops, sea turtles, red snapper, mullet, Spanish mackerel, pompano, and many more.

Arkansas grows rice in modern artificially irrigated fields. With her varied terrain and climate, she also produces corn, Irish and sweet potatoes, sorghums, apples, peaches, strawberries, watermelons, and pecans.

Louisiana is a principal rice-producing state. Sugar cane, strawberries, sweet potatoes, corn, pecans, and peanuts are also leading crops. From Louisiana's waters are taken shrimp, oysters, crabs, frog legs, and diamondback terrapin, and from the farther reaches of the Gulf come redfish, sea trout, king and Spanish mackerel, red snapper, and pompano.

RECIPES OF THE
SOUTH TO TRY

HUSH PUPPIES

(Makes about 30 to 36)

2	cups finely ground white corn meal
2	teaspoons baking powder
1½	teaspoons salt
¼	teaspoon white pepper
1	egg, beaten
¼	cup water
¾	cup milk
2	tablespoons very finely diced onion

In a bowl combine the corn meal, baking powder, salt, and pepper. Mix together the beaten egg, water, and milk. Add to the dry ingredients and blend smooth. Add the onions.

Into a deep heavy skillet, pour cooking oil to a depth of ¼ inch. Allow oil to get hot and then drop teaspoonfuls of the hush-puppy mixture into the skillet. Each hush puppy should be about the size of a large walnut. Fry until golden brown on bottom, turn and fry other side. Drain hush puppies on absorbent paper, and serve hot with fried fish, seafood, or chicken.

SOUTHERN PECAN PIE

(one 8- or 9-inch pie)

1	8- or 9-inch unbaked pie shell (Use a commercially prepared pie shell, make up pastry from commercial mix, or use own favorite recipe.)
½	cup butter or margarine (¼ pound)

⅔   cup dark brown sugar
3   eggs, beaten
¾   cup white corn sirup
⅛   teaspoon salt
1   teaspoon vanilla
1   cup pecan halves

Place butter or margarine in a bowl and cream it with the back of a wooden spoon until it is soft and smooth. Add brown sugar, blend well, and beat until smooth. Combine the beaten eggs with the corn sirup, salt, and vanilla. Add to the butter and brown sugar mixture and blend well. Add pecan halves.

Turn pie filling into pastry shell. Bake at 425 degrees for 10 minutes, then reduce heat to 300 degrees and bake 30 to 35 minutes longer, or until a sharp knife inserted into the center of the pie comes out clean.

Serve Southern Pecan Pie cool or chilled, plain or with whipped cream or vanilla ice cream. This is a very rich pie, so cut it into small portions.

the midwest and the great plains

Ohio Minnesota
Indiana Iowa
Illinois Missouri
Michigan North Dakota
Wisconsin South Dakota
Nebraska
Kansas
Oklahoma

Between the Allegheny Mountains and the Rockies lies the great heartland of the United States. This is the land of the persimmon, the papaw, and the hickory nut. It is also the natural habitat of a seven-foot grass known as wild rice, of a brown-plumaged bird called a prairie chicken, and of the buffalo, a shaggy-bearded beast weighing as much as 2,000 pounds.

Where does the Midwest begin? Its eastern Ohio boundary is hilly and wooded, but in the western part of the state the rolling grasslands of the prairie commence. Across the states of Indiana, Illinois, Iowa, and Missouri and into eastern Nebraska and Kansas this "sea of grass" continues. One of the richest agricultural tracts of the nation, it is popularly known as the corn belt.

Beyond the prairie lie the Great Plains, drier, more level, and almost completely treeless for 500 miles. Although the plains appear perfectly flat, they actually increase in elevation as they travel westward toward the foothills of the Rockies. Lying as they do in the shadow of great mountains, the plains receive little rainfall. Their natural vegetation is a low-growing matted grass known as buffalo grass. Although hundreds of pioneers crossed the plains on their way to Oregon and California, most travelers considered this region unfit for cultivation and referred to it as the Great American Desert. As a result, the plains states of the Dakotas, Nebraska, Kansas, and Oklahoma were among the last to be settled.

Four of the Great Lakes—Erie, Huron, Michigan, and Superior—are in the Midwest. The Mississippi and the Missouri cut great swaths through the country. But the sea, with its moderating effect on climate, is a considerable distance from this vast inland region. Therefore the winters tend to be long and cold, and the summers very hot. In the plains states especially, bitter gales in winter and hot drying blasts in summer sweep across the unbroken expanse of the land.

In the extreme western portions of the Dakotas and Nebraska are the famous Bad Lands, a dry country of sandstone buttes sculptured into fantastic shapes by wind and rain erosion. The Bad Lands are in a sense wasteland, but their wild scenic beauty cannot be denied.

FROM MOUND BUILDERS TO BUFFALO HUNTERS

The Indian tribes of the Midwest and the Great Plains were members of three of the great North American Indian families: the Algonquian, the Siouan, and the Caddoan.

When the first white settlers arrived in Ohio and in the Great Lakes country, they found numerous Indian tribes, most of them members of the same Algonquian family that had inhabited New England, the coastal region of the Middle Atlantic States, and Virginia. Some of these Midwestern tribes were the Chippewa (also called Ojibway), the Menominee, Miami, Shawnee, Sac, and Fox.

But these were not the original inhabitants of these lands. Scattered throughout Illinois, Wisconsin, and other states, but especially in Ohio, are odd-shaped earthworks known as mounds, believed to have been built by a prehistoric people who were the ancestors of the American Indian that the white man came to know. These huge man-made mounds, which were built in square, octagonal, and circular shapes, and even in the likenesses of serpents and other animals, were used as burial places, fortifications, and places of worship.

From seeds found in these mounds we learn that the

Mound Builders cultivated corn, squash, and beans just as the Indians of a later day did. The presence of numerous stone pipes indicates that the Mound Builders probably grew and smoked tobacco, and their collections of pearls, often used to adorn their dead, are believed to have been taken from fresh-water clams dug along the banks of the Ohio and its tributaries. Flint arrowheads and bone hunting knives are evidence of their having killed and eaten wild animals.

For the Indians who came to these Midwestern lands centuries later, life was very similar. Corn, tobacco, pumpkins, squash, melons, and beans were grown wherever the soil and climate were favorable. The tribes of the Great Lakes country were especially skilled in the use of birch bark, which was plentiful along the lake shores. Not only canoes, but wigwam sheathings, picture-writing "paper," and leakproof cooking pots that could be used for boiling food over an open fire were made of birch bark.

Because corn was difficult to grow in the evergreen forests that lined the Minnesota, Wisconsin, and Michigan shores of Lake Superior, the Indians of this region turned to a wild grass for their grain. In the reedy shallows and backwaters of the lake grew the seven-foot-tall wild rice which the early colonists, many of whom were unacquainted with rice, referred to as wild oats, or wild wheat. In reality this cereal food was neither rice nor oats nor wheat, but a wild grain-bearing perennial grass of semiaquatic habit. Like rice it grew best with its "feet in the water."

The Indians, gliding through the water in boats, harvested this grain by shaking the ripe ears directly into their canoes. The grain was then dried by smoking over an open fire. To winnow the rice, or separate the seed from the chaff, the Indians poured it into skin bags which they then vigorously trampled on. Then they pounded the kernels to make flour, or they cooked them whole in water, seasoning the rice with bear fat or with butternut or sunflower oil.

Harvesting time for wild rice was in September, and although the Indians of the rice country did not have the work of cultivation as did the corn-growing Indians, the processing of the seed was a lengthy and fatiguing task. This job fell chiefly to the women of the tribe. Wild rice is today a luxury food, still hand-harvested by the Indians in many parts of the Great Lakes country. Most of the Indians, however, have forsaken wild rice in their own diets, for its cost is roughly twenty times that of cultivated true rice.

Wherever stands of sugar maples were to be found, the Indians of the Ohio country and the Lakes region manufactured maple sirup and maple sugar, just as the Iroquois of central New York and the Algonquians of New England did.

The persimmon, a native American fruit found in many parts of the South, was also plentiful in certain areas of the Midwest, particularly in what is now Ohio and Indiana. French fur traders traveling in the prairie country of the Midwest in the late 1600s wrote of trees laden with "apples" which tasted so bad that they could not be eaten unless they had first been left to freeze.

This fruit was undoubtedly the small red-orange persimmon, so puckery until frost-nipped that it turns the tongue to sandpaper. But when allowed to ripen until the first hard frost, its pulp seems miraculously transformed into a smooth sweet-tasting flesh. The Indians ate this fruit both raw and cooked, preparing it with other foods. They also made bread, using the dried seeds of the persimmon pounded into flour.

The Ohio and Indiana settlers were later to use the persimmon in puddings, pies, and in a jam or "butter." They also used the pulp in a persimmon bread which they considered far superior to gingerbread. Persimmons sometimes appear in fruit markets today, but they are most likely to be an Oriental variety of the fruit, much larger than the native American persimmon and almost completely seedless.

Crabapples, grapes, plums, and cherries were also plentiful in the Midwest, but the French traders and explorers complained of the first two being exceedingly sour and of poor quality. The plums, not much better, were thick-skinned and very different in flavor from the excellent cultivated plums of France.

But the native blackberries, large and juicy, and the odd-looking papaw met with approval. The papaw is an oblong yellowish fruit which somewhat resembles a banana, but its flavor is so bland that it has never become popular. It is sometimes confused with the tropical papaya, but the two are not related.

All of the fruits mentioned, however, were eaten by the Indians. In addition there were nuts of many varieties— black walnuts, hard-shelled hickories, oil-rich butternuts, and tiny tasty chinquapins, or dwarf chestnuts, which the Indians roasted over open fires.

The lakes and streams were literally crowded with fish. In the Great Lakes and in the northern lakes of Michigan, Wisconsin, and Minnesota were trout, bass, pike, pickerel, whitefish, and lake herring. The French fur traders wrote of fish taken by the Indians that were so huge there was an expanse of 18 inches between their eyes! In the Mississippi and in the smaller rivers perch, eel, and catfish were caught. The Indians prepared their fish in a variety of ways, boiling, roasting, or smoking it. A favorite dish was sagamité, a mixture of fish and corn meal cooked together in water and seasoned with elk or moose marrow, or with bear fat. Like their predecessors the Mound Builders, the Indians of the

Midwest dug fresh-water clams along the banks of the Ohio, and also along the Mississippi.

Game birds were probably more plentiful in this lake and prairie region than anywhere else in the country—grouse; partridge (also called bobwhite or quail) ; canvasbacks and other varieties of wild duck; wild geese; and of course wild turkeys. The prairie chicken, a variety of grouse native to the open prairie, was prized for its delicious flesh. In amazement a French traveler of the late 1600s wrote in his memoirs of a lake in the Illinois country, its surface so completely covered with bird life in autumn that had the flocks remained on the water, an Indian canoe could not have passed among them. Yet this lake was over twenty miles long!

Deer, elk, moose, and bear, as well as smaller animals, were game for the Indians of the Midwest, and from the prairies westward to the Great Plains roamed the herds of buffalo (zoologically classified as bison) .

The Indians of the Great Plains were known as the Buffalo Hunters. Unlike the lake country and prairie Indians of the Midwest, they undertook little or no agriculture. One reason for this was the surface of the plains themselves, a matted grass underlaid with thick twisting roots. The settlers who later broke the plains for agriculture were to be called sod-busters, but the primitive agricultural tools of the Indians were poorly suited to this task.

Another drawback to the planting of crops on the plains was their extreme dryness. Rainfall was uncertain, and sources of irrigation such as streams and rivers were too far apart or too likely to run dry to keep growing crops watered.

A few of the plains tribes maintained two villages, one permanent village for summer use located on fertile land near a river bed, where they grew some vegetable food—corn, beans, and squash. The women tended the corn patches while the men organized themselves into hunting parties. At other seasons of the year the entire tribe might become nomadic, following the lusher grasslands which the buffalo frequented.

We are so accustomed to the image of the Plains Indian mounted on a galloping horse in pursuit of a herd of buffalo that we are apt to forget that before the Spanish explored

North America in the 1500s the Indians had no horses. Only in prehistoric times did the horse exist on the American continent. It is believed that the ancestors of the American Indian hunted the horse for food, thus causing it to become extinct.

So the Indians hunted buffalo on foot before the coming of the white man. They stampeded the buffalo by constructing a "trap" in the form of a funnel, its narrow end culminating on the edge of a cliff. Piles of stones bordered the V-shaped outline of the trap. When a herd approached the area of the trap, the Indians, by prodding, lured the leaders of the herd into the wide mouth of the funnel. The rest of the beasts followed and the Indian hunters, shouting and waving robes along the sidelines, harried the buffalo into a headlong stampede over the cliff. It was then a simple matter to kill the wounded animals in the pit below.

The lack of horses made the transport of the slaughtered buffalo difficult. A travois, or pack frame fastened to two poles, was harnessed to a dog and served to carry the cut-up carcasses back to the Indian village. Most hunting in those days was, of necessity, carried on close to home.

Once the Spanish swept across the lower half of the plains leaving stray horses in their wake, the Indian became a mounted hunter. The Indian was a natural horseman and his prowess at hunting buffalo over great distances was unequaled. Herds of elk and deer were also hunted for food on the plains.

Although the Algonquians are thought of chiefly as woodland and agricultural Indians, tribes of this family—the Blackfoot, Cheyenne, and Arapaho—did inhabit the plains, where they lived as buffalo hunters along with the Dakota, Mandan, and Crow tribes of the Siouan family, and the Pawnee, a plains tribe of the Caddoan family.

So completely did the Plains Indian depend on the buffalo that almost no part of the animal was wasted. His flesh served for food, his horns for spoons, his ribs for sharp curved knives, and his tendons for thread with which to sew the buffalo hides that the Indian fashioned into robes, moccasins, and tepees.

Even cooking pots were made from the skin of the buffalo.

Into a bowl-shaped hole dug in the ground a cleaned skin would be carefully placed as a lining. This "pot" would then be filled with water, chunks of buffalo meat, and possibly some vegetables. To cook the stew, the Indians used a method known as stone-boiling. Red-hot stones which had been heated in the fire were added to the pot until the water began to boil and the stew was eventually cooked. This method was slow and tiresome, however, for the stones had constantly to be removed, reheated, and re-added to the pot, and bits of ash and grit were almost sure to add themselves to the ingredients of the stew.

Buffalo meat was also roasted or broiled over an open campfire. The udders and the tongues of the buffalo were considered choice bits by the Indians; the humps and the marrow bones were also well liked. In winter the buffalo grew thin, but by midsummer the buffalo was fat again and the older animals, especially, yielded much tallow. Summer and fall, therefore, were favorite seasons for buffalo hunting.

The kill of a good season's hunting was preserved by drying. The meat was cut into paper-thin strips and dried either in the hot sun or over the heat of a smoky fire. It was then rolled up tightly in strips of bark or dried skin, thirty to forty pieces to the package. Thus preserved, buffalo meat might keep as long as five years. Venison was also prepared this way, and later frontiersmen and plainsmen learned to prepare beef in this fashion.

The dried meat product was known as jerk, or jerky. The word is derived from the Spanish *charque* or *charqui* of Peruvian origin, referring to meat dried in the sun. To prepare jerked buffalo meat, the Indians pounded it with stones to a powder and cooked it in water, possibly adding a little corn meal. It was also chewed on in its dry form as an emergency ration.

Pemmican was a fancier version of jerky. To make pemmican, the Indians beat the jerked meat into shreds with sticks, then added some dried wild berries and melted buffalo tallow. They formed the mixture into little cakes which were then packed tightly into bags of buffalo skin. Since it kept indefinitely as long as it was protected from moisture, Indian pemmican so favorably impressed white scouts and hunters that it was later used as a long-keeping nourishing food by members of Arctic expeditions.

The Indian tribes of the plains achieved their peak of success as buffalo hunters through the gifts of the white man —the horse, and later gunpowder and the rifle. By 1800 most plains Indians had come into possession of horses, and a golden age of hunting and travel was under way.

But this glorious time for the Indian was to be short-lived. By 1840 the advancing frontier of the white settlers was beginning to make itself felt in the buffalo country, having already pushed many Midwestern tribes westward. Then in 1849 the gold rush to California brought wagon trains across the plains themselves. After the Civil War, professional white hunters invaded the plains, killing the buffalo for their skins. The Homestead Act of 1862 and the completion of the transcontinental railroad in 1869 made further inroads upon the Plains Indians' territory.

The Indian did not submit to the extinction of the life-giving buffalo without a struggle. There were repeated bloody and tragic encounters between the Indians of the plains and the cavalry troops of the white man. But by 1885 the buffalo was no more. The government came to the aid of the defeated Indian with crackers, flour, and salt pork, but fresh juicy buffalo meat and the rigorous, challenging life of the hunt were things of the past. In a country ill-suited to primitive agriculture, the destiny of most of the plains tribes was the enforced and demoralizing idleness of life on the reservation.

FRONTIER LIFE IN THE OLD NORTHWEST

Although the Great Lakes country and the upper Mississippi Valley were first explored by the French during the late 1600s, this Midwestern territory was to be settled a century later by American colonists moving westward. From Virginia, the Middle Atlantic, and the New England colonies, pioneer families crossed the Alleghenies and made their way into what was then termed the "Northwest."

This area was northwesterly, of course, only in relation to

the already settled regions of the eastern seaboard. Not to confuse it with the true Northwest of modern times (the Pacific states of Washington and Oregon) , it is today referred to as the "Old Northwest." The famous Ordinance of 1787 provided a plan for the government of the Northwest Territory, a tract of land comprised of what is now Ohio, Indiana, Illinois, Michigan, Wisconsin, and part of Minnesota.

By wagon, by pack horse, on foot, and afloat (on Ohio River flatboats) , the settlers trekked into the new territory. In 1788 Marietta, Ohio, the first town in the Northwest Territory, was founded. Ohio, the opening state of this new segment of the country, has been called "the crossroads of an expanding America."

Frontier life in the Northwest Territory was in many respects a repetition of colonial life on the Atlantic coast nearly 200 years earlier. Corn was the first crop to be planted. The land was still covered with dense first-growth forest, and since clearing the ground was a taxing and time-consuming job, many settlers used the Indian method of girdling the trees to provide sunshine for the cornstalks growing on the forest floor.

Wild turkey, bear, deer, and elk were plentiful. Hungry settlers even ate panther. Reddish-furred and with a long thick tail, this native American member of the cat family was also known as the puma, cougar, and mountain lion. It stalked the forests in search of young deer and later molested the sheep, calves, and other domestic animals of the new settlers.

Smaller animals of all sorts found their way into the cooking pot. Porcupines and other "varmints" were eaten when the pickings were poor, but opossum, squirrel, and rabbit made tasty stews. Pigs and chickens were brought to the frontier quite early. Pigs were especially well adapted to life in these wild surroundings, for they rooted in the woods, killing and eating rattlesnakes with no injurious effects to themselves.

Still the settlers longed for bread. As with the frontiersmen of Kentucky and Tennessee, the white meat of turkey often served this purpose because of its contrast to the stronger-flavored, gamier quality of other wild meat. Corn meal was an indispensable part of the provisions the pioneers brought with them into the new territory. Its use was rationed carefully until the dried kernels of the first new crop had been ground into meal.

On the frontier corn was ground in a stone hand mill or was grated on a perforated tin grater nailed to a block of wood. The coarse, uneven granules produced were sieved through a piece of deerskin punched with holes. Corn bread, in one form or another, was a part of every meal eaten on the frontier. The johnnycake of New England and the corn pone and hoecake of Virginia all traveled to the Midwest. Corn-meal mush was a universal breakfast and supper dish, often the only dish served at these meals. Hominy with a gravy of meat juices or with wild honey was also served frequently.

Pumpkins, squash, potatoes, beans, and cabbage were planted as soon as possible after the corn went in. Potpie was a favorite main dish. It was not a pie but a stew of vegetables and meat, to which dumplings were added. Spoon meats or stews were easiest to cook and eat, and also kept best.

Salt, for preserving meat, was not always available on the frontier. It was also extremely expensive, a barrel of salt shipped from the East costing as much as nine or ten dollars. Some pioneers banded into groups and made yearly expeditions to areas where there were salt licks. (The city of French Lick in Indiana was named for both its French ancestry and its salt deposits, which attracted animals as well as salt-hungry settlers.) Here the frontiersmen evaporated enough salt to last until the next expedition. But many Midwesterners dried their meat without salt over the smoke of the fire, Indian fashion. This, of course, was jerk, prepared most often from venison or beef.

Pumpkins and squashes, too, were preserved by drying. Dried beans, the staple of New England, also came westward, and baked beans became a standard frontier dish. Cabbage was best preserved in the form of sauerkraut. Milk did not keep well, and naturally fermented sour milk soon came into common use as both a cooking ingredient and a drink. Coffee and tea were scorned on the frontier as overcivilized beverages. Tea of a sort was made, however, from spicewood and from sassafras. It was served mainly to the elderly, to the invalided, and to the sick, and it was taken in spring as a tonic to "purify the blood."

Whisky was distilled and drunk from the earliest days of settlement. It had the virtue of keeping indefinitely without spoiling and offered cheer, warmth, and stimulation to the harsh, often grim days on the frontier. More important, it was both an antiseptic and a painkiller, the only medicine of the wilderness. For snakebite, for toothache, as an anesthetic in the treatment of wounds and during the amputations that were often necessitated by tragic accidents, whisky had no peer. While it is true that its used was often abused, we cannot underrate its importance in the lives of the pioneers.

Fresh green vegetables and fruits were always a treat in a country where game and meal were the principal foods. The first "roasting ears" of corn were eagerly awaited on the frontier, and wild greens were gathered at the earliest sign of spring. The abundance of wild berries, persimmons, and other native fruits was much enhanced by the introduction of the apple.

The states of Ohio, Indiana, and Illinois look on the famed Johnny Appleseed as their benefactor. From the early 1800s on, this strangely attired visionary was seen wandering through the countryside planting apple orchards in whatever fertile areas he could locate. On return missions he tended and transplanted the young trees so that soon even the crudest frontier cabin was graced with a few fruit-bearing apple trees.

Johnny Appleseed has become such a legend in American folklore that few recall his true identity. He was born John Chapman in Boston in 1775. Both a vegetarian and a religious disciple of Emanuel Swedenborg, a Swedish mystic and philosopher, Chapman chose to spend forty years in the wilderness planting apple trees and preaching the Gospel. He is said to have gone barefoot most of the time, clad only in a rude coffee sack.

Although apple trees are most often propagated by grafting, Johnny Appleseed denounced this method of cultivation as sinful, growing his trees only from seeds, most of which he obtained from the waste material of the cider presses of western Pennsylvania. This "patron saint of American orchards" is believed to have carried his mission as far west as Iowa. He is buried in Johnny Appleseed Park in Fort Wayne, Indiana.

Thanks to the thriving young apple orchards, apple butter was soon being made on the frontier. Sugar was scarce in the early days, but wild honey was often available, and settlers having a grove of sugar maples made their own maple sirup and maple sugar. Later, when sugar became more plentiful, preserved crabapples, persimmon butter (a jamlike spread of persimmon pulp and sugar), and berry preserves were put up in quantity each season.

Homes, fireplaces, and cooking utensils were crude in the early days on the frontier. The abundance of wood and the

scarcity of metals, pottery, and tools led to ingenious methods of producing tableware. Porringers for serving mush and
milk, as well as larger mixing bowls, were made by burning
holes in blocks of wood, then chipping and scraping at the
charred portions until they had been sufficiently hollowed
out. Wooden spoons were used for eating, few forks were
available, and the hunter's knife was used at table for
all cutting.

Metals were not to be had west of the Alleghenies for
many years, and no pioneer from the East would dream of
setting out without at least one treasured iron kettle or stew
pot. A bake kettle with cover and handle, not quite as deep
as a stew pot, was also useful for steamed puddings and porridges. A spider was also commonly used in the pioneer
household. This three-legged iron frying pan, with a lid,
could be set right over the fire. It was essential for frying
foods and was also used for making spider corn bread. A
gridiron was needed for broiling or grilling meat and for
toasting johnnycake.

Just as in the early years in New England, the green-wood
lug pole, set across the inside of the fireplace where it rested
on ledges, was the order of the day. The stew pot or bake
kettle hung from it, and the lug pole had to be watched for
signs of drying and charring lest it break and tumble the
entire dinner into the flames. Joints of roasting meat hung
over the fire by a rawhide thong and were given a spin now
and then for even cooking. Metal spits and elaborate turning mechanisms such as were used back East were rare indeed.

House raisings, barn raisings, weddings, quilting bees and
husking bees, nutting parties, apple cuttings, and taffy pulls
were all occasions for festivity on the frontier. Many of these
combined work with play. House raisings and weddings were
particularly gay with much drinking and feasting, often last-
ing two days or more. Pranks and hilarity reigned at frontier
weddings, but the bride and groom took these in good
grace knowing they in turn would soon be guests at some
other couple's wedding. Potpie was the standard dish at
most frontier weddings, house raisings, and other community gatherings.

Quilting parties, or bees, served a useful purpose, for while the men indulged in games and drinking, the women, who had eaten their supper first, sewed scraps of cloth together for a fancy pieced quilt top. They then stitched the top to a plain linen backing with a layer of wool in between. Many hands made the work go quickly to the tunes of gossip and laughter.

Since the Revolutionary War had ended only a short time before the settlement of the Midwest began, the Fourth of July was a time of all-out celebration on the frontier. Pioneer families drove to the nearest town to hear orations and witness military displays, or simply gathered together to barbecue a sheep or hog, drink toasts, indulge in shooting contests and games of skill, or exhibit feats of strength. If a fiddler was present, there was sure to be much jollity and dancing far into the night.

Each season of the year brought its occasion for merriment, but one season that brought only foreboding on the frontier was Indian summer. This was the period of warm, still weather that often came in October following the first cool days and frosty nights of autumn. It was the time of harvest, of hog butchering, and of stocking the woodpile for winter. It was also a time when the Indians made their final ravages before the onset of winter, coming for horses, livestock, the fruits of the pioneer's harvest—and, tragically, for scalps.

The Americans of the Eastern seaboard who trekked westward in the early 1800s were soon to be joined by settlers from many lands of Europe. German, Dutch, Swiss, Scandinavian, and Cornish immigrants seeking religious and political freedom, employment, new farmlands, and other benefits, arrived from about the 1830s on, bringing about a vast increase in population and enriching the productivity of the Midwest. In a sense the drama that had taken place on the Atlantic coast two hundred years earlier was now

AMERICAN AND FOREIGN INFLUENCES ON MIDWESTERN COOKERY

being re-enacted. To the natural food resources of the region, these colorful foreign peoples brought their own national heritages and developed new cuisines that came to be called Michigan Dutch, Wisconsin German, and Minnesota Scandinavian.

From observations of the Great Lakes and prairie Indians, we are acquainted with the native foods of the Midwest. The pioneer families of the Midwestern frontier used these foods, adding traditional dishes that they brought from the East: baked beans, succotash, and johnnycake from New England; fried chicken and cream gravy from the South; relishes, pickles, and fruit butters from the Pennsylvania Dutch country.

The pioneers from older settled areas also adapted many foods to the special resources of the new region. To pumpkin pie, for example, former New Englanders now added chopped black walnuts, flavor-rich nuts native to the Midwest. Cakes, cookies, and frostings were graced with these nuts, and black-walnut fudge has remained a popular Midwestern confection to this day. Hickory nuts, too, although troublesome to extract from their shells, became an ingredient of cookies and other baked goods, and especially of Indiana hickory-nut cake.

On the shores of Lake Michigan, where the climate was tempered by the presence of a large body of water, wild cherry trees grew. With the introduction of improved varie-

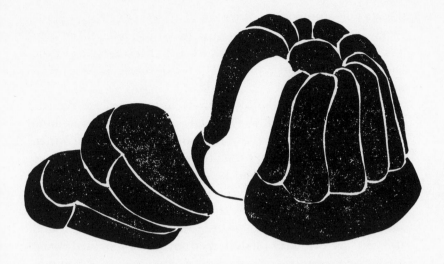

ties and the establishment of orchards, cherries of good quality were soon being produced in abundance. Here in the Midwest transplanted New Englanders baked cherry cobbler instead of blueberry grunt, and Michigan cherry pie instead of Cape Cod cranberry pie.

Steamed persimmon pudding, persimmon pie, and persimmon butter were favorites in Ohio, Indiana, and other Midwestern states. They are still made today from old family recipes, for the mellow sweet pulp of this native fruit was used by the earliest settlers.

Angel-food cake, so named because of its fluffy whiteness and delicate texture, is said to have been "invented" in St. Louis, Missouri. Actually, angel food is a derivative of Old World spongecake. No butter, fat, or other shortening is used in spongecake, whose richness depends on the use of eggs, especially the yolks. For angel-food cake only the stiffly beaten whites of eggs are included, thus producing a tender mile-high cake. Because angel food is not very rich, it is often served with ice cream or with strawberry or chocolate sauce.

Angel-food cake could only have been developed in an area where poultry farming was prevalent and eggs therefore plentiful, for one cake requires at least one cup or about eight to ten egg whites. It also requires a strong beating arm, and the luxury of sufficient labor and time to whip the air into the whites. Since Missouri was one of the slave states, it is almost certain that the first angel-food cakes were baked by Negro slaves brought up the Mississippi from the deep South to work the cotton plantations of her south-eastern Delta region.

In the late 1800s, the soybean was introduced for cultivation in the Midwest. This Oriental legume, known in China and Japan for centuries, is a rich source of important nutrients and supplies numerous products from animal feed to plastics. Its food uses alone are so extensive that the soybean has crept into the cookery of the Midwest, where soybean muffins (made with part soybean flour and part wheat flour) and salted soybeans (the "salted peanuts" of Michigan and Illinois) are everyday foods. Green soybeans, too, are cooked and served as a green vegetable or combined with onions, celery, green pepper, and tomatoes for a golden crumb-topped soybean scallop.

Game and wild fowl were so plentiful in the Midwest that even after domestic hogs, beef cattle, sheep, and poultry were brought to the new region, fried rabbit, broiled venison steak, and roast canvasback duck remained popular meat and poultry courses. For homesick Southerners the wild prairie chicken provided a dish very much like the fried chicken of the South. Really a variety of grouse, this native fowl of the prairie could be prepared exactly like chicken. Fried prairie chicken, crisp and tender, was usually served in the Southern tradition, with cream gravy.

Later, when prairie chicken became scarce because of extensive hunting and the domestication of its prairie habitat, the ring-necked pheasant was introduced from England. The pheasant has thrived well as a game bird in the settled farming country of the Midwest and plains states, and is much sought after by sportsmen. It is delicious braised, roasted, or stewed.

Of wild ducks, the canvasback is especially prized. Its habit of eating wild celery roots imparts a delicious flavor to its flesh. Wild celery is native to the lake regions of the Midwest, but its bitter flavor and tough woody texture make it unsatisfactory as food for man. It is even considered poison-

ous by some. So well suited, however, to celery growing are the "muck" soils bordering Lake Michigan that in modern times Michigan has become prominent in the cultivation of crisp tender edible varieties of celery.

Mallard ducks are another variety valued at table. Their food consists largely of wild rice and other pond or lake shore grasses. Mergansers, on the other hand, are fish-eating ducks. Their flesh has an unpleasant fishy flavor and is not considered good eating.

In most places game laws have been passed to restrict the hunter, so that the once plentiful grouse, ducks, and other wild fowl of the lakes and prairie region will not be exterminated. Nevertheless many game birds once so widely distributed in the Midwest that they were daily fare on the dinner

tables of frontier cabins have now become luxury foods.

From the common lake herring, most abundant food fish in the Great Lakes, to the 8-foot muskellunge, a prized game fish of northern waters, the Midwest is well supplied with fresh-water fish. Black bass with almonds and mushrooms, planked Lake Superior whitefish (baked on a wooden plank edged with frills of fluffy mashed potatoes), broiled trout, and baked pike are all superb regional fish offerings.

Smelts, a comparative newcomer to the Midwestern lake country, were transplanted from New England waters in 1912 to serve as food for larger species. They throve exceedingly well, and have become a particular favorite in the Midwest. Small silvery smelts are most frequently eaten baked with bacon, or dipped in egg and cracker meal and fried in deep fat.

DUTCH COOKERY IN THE MIDWEST

To all of the foregoing regional dishes of the Midwest, the pioneer immigrants of the mid-1800s added their own colorful Old World touches.

In 1847 religious refugees from the Netherlands settled the town of Holland, Michigan. Other Dutch towns soon sprang up, some as far off as Iowa, but all were patterned after the villages of the homeland. Tulip growing has since become an important industry in the Michigan Dutch towns. Every May in Holland, Michigan, and also in Pella, Iowa, tulip festivals are held—complete with Dutch costumes, parades, street-scrubbing ceremonies, and incomparable Dutch food.

The early Dutch immigrants spent their winters hunting and trapping fur-bearing animals for both food and pelts. In the summer they farmed whatever land they had been able to clear of trees. Long famous for their smoked and salted fish, their roast goose and other fowl, the Dutch took well to the fish and game birds of the new land. Having been waterside dwellers in their homeland, the Dutch were fond of fish and skilled in its preparation.

The lake herrings of the Great Lakes were not unlike the sea herrings of Holland, and the Dutch were soon much at home serving up fresh herring with onion sauce, or salting herrings for longer keeping. It has been said that no one can prepare smoked eels like the Dutch. Their method was to smoke the eels hanging tail-down in a barrel until the oil ran out of them. This process imparted to the eels a superb flavor. In the New World, the Mississippi and other rivers of the Midwest were a source of eels, which swarmed inland from the sea during the warmer months. Fresh eels were cut into one and one-half-inch lengths and simmered in salted water with parsley to make a dish known as *gestoofde aal* (stewed eel). Many Americans are not attracted to eel because of its snakelike appearance, but the Dutch who, like many Europeans, had used eel for countless generations, demonstrated its virtues to their neighbors in the new land.

Rye and whole-grain bread and hearty soups made with dried vegetables had long been standbys in the Dutch cuisine. Hence the newly settled Dutch farmers were soon growing wheat and other cereal grains, peas, beans, and root vegetables for their well-liked graham (whole-grain wheat) bread, their *roggebrood* (rye bread), and their *boonensoep* (bean soup).

Fruit, berry, and wine soups were also Old World specialties of the Dutch, just as they were popular among the Poles, Russians, and Scandinavians. These beautifully colored soups were served cold and made a delightful first course or main dish in hot weather. In the New World, the Dutch used wild blackberries in their fruit soups and were soon cultivating the red currants of northern Europe for this purpose. Later, when cherry and apple orchards became established, these fruits were also used in cold soups. For flavoring, the Dutch added cinnamon, nutmeg, cloves, and other spices which, in the homeland, had long been imported from the Pacific colonies of the Netherlands. *Wijnsoep* (wine soup) was a sweet soup prepared with raisins, lemon juice, and native grape wine or sherry. Barley was used as a thickening agent in the Dutch fruit and wine soups.

Apples from the New World orchards were, of course, an important ingredient in the renowned *Hollandsche appel koek* (Dutch apple cake), a yeast batter topped with tart-sweet apple slices and sprinkled with cinnamon and sugar. *Appelgebak* (apple bake) was a rich pudding of applesauce, stale bread crumbs, eggs, butter, sugar, and spices. Pickled cherries, which the Dutch served as a relish with meats and poultry, were sour Michigan cherries preserved in sugar and vinegar.

Flavored milk drinks were a vital part of the Dutch culinary tradition, and Dutch farmers of the Midwest were soon raising dairy cattle to supply milk for such beverages as licorice-flavored *anijsmelk* (anise milk, prepared with sugar and crushed anise seed) and delicious Dutch hot chocolate.

GERMAN COOKERY
IN THE MIDWEST

The Germans, like the Dutch, were to make two major immigrations to the New World. More than two hundred years after the settlement of New Amsterdam, the Dutch came as pioneer farmers headed for the Midwest. For the Germans, the first area of settlement had been the Pennsylvania country, in the late 1600s. Then, from the 1830s on, following political unrest and revolution in their homeland, great numbers of German immigrants began to arrive in Ohio, Missouri, Iowa, Minnesota, Wisconsin, and Michigan.

The largest influx spanned the period of the mid-century

to about 1890, with cities like Cincinnati, St. Louis, and Milwaukee taking on strong German cultural patterns, and reflecting in their cuisines the satisfying and hearty aspects of German cookery. Smaller communities, too, were established, and many of these towns still survive, with German-speaking populations bound by close-knit family and religious ties.

The cookery of the Midwest owes much to the stews and gravy-rich pot roasts of the German immigrants. Surely *hasenpfeffer* (pickled rabbit stew) must have been one of the first dishes that the German settlers cooked in their New World homes. This dish is similar to the German *sauerbraten* (sweet-and-sour pot roast), for the rabbit, cut into serving portions, is first marinated for two days in a mixture of vinegar, water, onion, and spices, just as the beef is for *sauerbraten*. The rabbit is then browned in hot butter or other fat, and simmered in some of the marinade until tender. At the very last, sour cream, if available, should be stirred into the gravy. This gives the stew a rich, mellow quality.

As domestic cattle increased and the new settlers became less dependent on rabbit and other game, veal emerged as a favored meat. Veal, the flesh of the calf, was eaten a great deal more in Europe than in America, but the immigrant influence has increased its use here, particularly in and around cities with large German or other foreign populations. From *schnitzel* (thin-sliced veal, often breaded) to stewed calves' tongues, roast veal, and veal loaf with sausages, this versatile meat is a standby in German-Midwestern cookery.

The German people have long been sausage makers par excellence, and they were quick to introduce the products of their skill to their new neighbors. So successful were the *wursts,* or sausages, of the newcomers that it was not long before German delicatessens opened in the larger towns and cities, offering for sale a wide variety of sausages and cold meats, sauerkraut, potato salad, pickles, cheeses, and all those mouth-watering delights that serve to remind us that the English translation of the German word, *delikatessen,* is "delicacies."

Sausage making is an important industry in the Midwest

to this day, with the city of Sheboygan, Wisconsin, celebrating an annual Bratwurst Festival each August, and many other areas also noted for their output of smoked sausages of German origin. But surely the most popular of all German *wursts* is the Frankfurt sausage, a highly seasoned beefand-pork or all-beef mixture stuffed into casings and linked. This sausage is better known, of course, as the frankfurter, named after the German city of its origin. (The hamburger, while not a sausage, is also German in derivation. For this chopped-beef mixture, once known as Hamburg steak, we owe a debt to the German city in which it originated and to the pioneer immigrants who brought it to America.)

Nearly as important as the German delicatessen was the German bakery. While most baking was done at home almost to the end of the nineteenth century, the influence of German baked goods was strong in the Midwest. In many cases, recipes for breads, rolls, and coffee cakes were passed from German housewives to their neighbors of other backgrounds. Some German women carried on small home-bakery businesses from their own kitchens. By the late 1800s, most Midwestern towns with German populations had commercial bakeries where hefty loaves of rye and pumpernickel bread, fragrant onion buns, crisp caraway-sprinkled salt sticks, and fat poppy-seed rolls could be carried home at very reasonable prices.

Coffeecakes, too, were a feature of the German bakery —raisin-and-almond-filled *stollen,* crumb-topped *streusel kuchen,* and *apfel kuchen* or other fruit-decorated yeast cakes using toppings of cherries, peaches, or plums as well as apples.

Käse kuchen (cheesecake) was another specialty of the German bakery. A rich mixture of cream or cottage cheese, eggs, and sweet cream, it was delicately flavored with lemon rind and coated with finely ground zwieback crumbs. Zwieback is a kind of rusk or small finger-shaped cake, toasted dry in the oven. Many German housewives baked it at home, for it was long-keeping and made an excellent supper dish broken into hot milk. The rich creamy cheesecakes featured today in many popular restaurants in New York City and elsewhere are usually prepared with a pastry rather than a zwieback crust, but they owe their origin to the *käse kuchen* of the German immigrant population.

Beer drinking was such a vital part of the German tradition that it is no surprise that the nation's largest brewing centers have developed in the Midwest and that most of the beers and ales produced in the United States today still bear the names of old German brewing families.

**SCANDINAVIAN
COOKERY IN
THE MIDWEST**

To the Scandinavian immigrants of the 1850s one of the most appealing features of life in Minnesota and Wisconsin was the excellent supply of fish. The plentiful lake herring alone provided the fish-loving Norwegian, Danish, and Swedish settlers with at least half a dozen familiar dishes from *fiskbullar* (fish balls) to *sillsallad* (herring salad). Dill, a favorite herb in Scandinavian cookery, was soon being used in the new land where baked pike with dill sauce was frequently prepared from the local variety of this fish. Salting, pickling, and smoking fish were all age-old Scandinavian arts, and the herrings and other fresh-water fish of the New World responded as well to these treatments as had the salt-water fish of northern Europe.

Minnesota, Wisconsin, and the Dakotas saw the peak of Scandinavian immigration during the 1880s. Pioneer life, particularly in the northern plains states, was indescribably harsh. But these stalwart people were soon planting grain and vegetables, and raising dairy cattle for the milk, cream, butter, and cheese that were an important part of their food heritage.

Cabbage, beets, potatoes, peas, and beans were soon yielding harvests for popular Scandinavian dishes—*rød kaal* (Danish red cabbage, cooked with vinegar and sugar, and often served with wild duck); beet-and-herring salad; creamed potatoes; Swedish potato salad; rib-sticking dried yellow split-pea soup; and brown beans with bacon, a dried-bean dish not unlike our New England baked beans.

Limpa (Swedish rye bread), *Norske Jule kake* (Norwegian Christmas bread), *Danska wienerbrød* (butter-rich Danish pastry), *kringler* and *spritz* cookies, and all sorts of coffee-cakes and tea rings were part of the array of handsome and fragrant baked goods that the Scandinavian peoples introduced to their neighbors in America. Ground cardamom seed, caraway seeds, and anise seed lend delicious and unusual flavorings to Scandinavian baking.

Swedish pancakes served with lingonberry sauce are a tra-

dition in Scandinavian cuisine. How fortunate that the lingonberry, a small wild cranberry that grows under semi-Arc-
tic conditions in Norway and Sweden, also grew in the bogs of
northern Wisconsin and Minnesota. Today, of course, cranberry cultivation has become an important industry in Wisconsin, just as it is in New Jersey and Massachusetts.

Like the Dutch, the Scandinavians had long used the red
currants native to northern Europe in their cookery. *Rød
grød* (red fruit-juice pudding) is considered the national
dessert of Denmark. Danish settlers in the Midwest were
soon cultivating the currant, for the juice of this tart red
berry, sweetened and thickened, is the substance of tan-
talizing ruby-toned *rød grød*. Native raspberries, strawberries,
plums, cherries, or gooseberries were, and still are, sometimes
added or substituted for currants in this dessert. On the
Scandinavian dairy farms of the New World, as in Denmark
itself, *rød grød* was most frequently served *med fløde* (with
cream) .

A most important feature of Scandinavian cookery and
food service is the smorgasbord, a display of assorted prepared foods, usually on a long table. The smorgasbord has
had an enormous influence on buffet serving here. In Sweden
and other Scandinavian countries the smorgasbord was devised as a means of providing large quantities of food for
guests who had traveled a long distance to attend weddings,
christenings, funerals, and the like. It was traditional for
each woman guest to bring along a dish of some prepared
food, usually her personal specialty, and to place it on the
smorgasbord table as her contribution to the enjoyment of all.

A smorgasbord may be quite simple, with only a few rep-
resentative dishes, or it may be very elaborate and extensive.
Dishes both hot and cold are included. All are beautifully
set forth and handsomely garnished, whether they are fish,
eggs, cheeses, cold meats, pickles and relishes, salads, or gelatin molds. Among the hot dishes, brown beans with bacon,
fish soufflés, scalloped potatoes, and *köttbullar* (Swedish meat
balls) are frequently offered.

In the Midwest, church suppers and other community

functions are more than likely to take on the pattern of the informal Scandinavian buffet meal, with those present helping themselves from the smorgasbord table, and then returning with heaping plates to sit at smaller tables with friends. While strictly Scandinavian specialties like *lutfisk* (dried imported cod served with melted butter or mustard sauce) may not appeal to the general taste, many smorgasbord items have become favorites in the Midwest and throughout the country. Outstanding among these are appetite-teasing pickled herring, delicate nutmeg-seasoned Swedish meat balls, macaroni salads in an onion-flavored mayonnaise or cream dressing, and jewel-like molded gelatin salads of cold meats or fish, crisp vegetables, or sparkling fruits.

Beer and *aquavit* are preferred alcoholic beverages among the Scandinavians. *Aquavit,* a dry colorless liquor with the flavor of caraway, is a potent drink that is probably best appreciated, in this country, by those of Scandinavian background. Beer has, of course, wide general appeal and is immensely popular in the Scandinavian-populated brewing centers of the Midwest.

SWISS AND CORNISH FOODS IN WISCONSIN

For Wisconsin's dairy production and enormous cheese output, many thanks are due the Swiss settlers who established the town of New Glarus in 1845. Having left the overcrowded Canton Glarus in Switzerland, these enterprising newcomers took up dairy farming in the lush pasture lands of southern Wisconsin. Soon they were making the Swiss cheese of their homeland, and laying the foundation for the cheese industry that thrives today in Wisconsin and in neighboring Illinois.

Americans most frequently eat Swiss cheese as a snack or sandwich food, but Swiss cookery uses this cheese in such dishes as Swiss cheese-and-onion pie and in Swiss fondue. Swiss fondue is a hot mixture of melted Swiss cheese, white wine, and *kirschwasser* (a brandy distilled from cherries). The fondue is seasoned with garlic and possibly a pinch of nutmeg.

Traditionally, the diners spear chunks of crusty French or Italian bread onto long "fondue" forks, then dip the bread into the faintly bubbling cheese mixture which is cooked in a chafing dish at the table. The bread, well coated with the delicious fondue, is then withdrawn and quickly popped into the mouth. The Swiss say that if a girl drops her chunk of bread into the fondue, the men at the table are permitted to kiss her.

Like most Europeans, the Swiss settlers of Wisconsin were fond of veal which they used in *kalbswurst* (veal sausage) and in veal *à la Suisse* (a braised veal dish prepared with sour cream and served with noodles).

Many Swiss customs, as well as Swiss cookery, have been preserved in Wisconsin's "Little Switzerland." The town of New Glarus is the scene of Swiss yodeling and Swiss music each August in celebration of Swiss Independence Day, and of a William Tell pageant which is held each year on the Labor Day weekend.

Another notable contribution to Wisconsin cuisine was introduced by the Cornishmen, who came as early as 1830 to work in the lead and zinc mines of the New World. These tin miners from Cornwall, the southwestern section of England, were seeking employment and a better way of life. Unfortunately the mines they had come to work in Wisconsin and in neighboring Michigan soon gave out. Some drifted westward in search of other mine work, while others went in for farming in the vicinity of former mining towns like Mineral Point in southern Wisconsin.

Thanks to these Cornishmen, Wisconsin now has a rich heritage of foods such as Cornish pasty, Cornish scones, English toffee pie, and Devonshire cream.

The Cornish pasty (pronounced pass-tee) is an individual meat-and-vegetable pie sealed in a pastry crust. Originally pasties were taken down into the mines by the Cornish workers to be eaten for lunch. Their popularity has not diminished over the years, and they may be sampled today in the old Cornish mining country of Wisconsin.

Cornwall, being part of England, has always favored scones with tea. Cornish scones are really rich baking-powder biscuits flavored with a touch of lemon.

Popular Cornish desserts are English toffee pie, its filling a mixture of cream, eggs, raisins, nuts, and sherry, and Devonshire cream. To prepare Devonshire cream a standing mixture of milk and cream is slowly heated in a shallow pan, then chilled. The "cream" which forms at the top has the consistency of soft cream cheese. It is skimmed off and eaten with fresh or preserved fruit as a dessert or it may be eaten with scones and jam at tea.

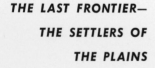

THE LAST FRONTIER— THE SETTLERS OF THE PLAINS

Over one hundred years were to pass between the founding of Marietta, Ohio, first town in the Northwest Territory, and the settlement of the last of the Great Plains farmlands in Oklahoma in 1889. During this period the frontier had begun to shift steadily westward toward the vast central portion of the United States. Then, at the threshold of the Great Plains—bleak, treeless, and wind-swept—the settlers had either held back or passed over on their way to Oregon and California.

Explorers and fur trappers, pony express riders, wagon trains, stagecoaches, and United States cavalry detachments were the itinerants of the plains for years, while much farther west, in the lush valleys of the Oregon country, nearly twenty thousand settlers had already made new homes.

Then in 1862 the Homestead Act was passed. This act provided that a qualified head of family could become the owner of a farm or homestead of 160 acres if he lived on it and farmed it for five years. With the Homestead Act serving as a spur, the close of the Civil War and the building of the railroads saw the settlement, at last, in the 1860s and 1870s of the Dakotas, Nebraska, and Kansas.

Many of the homesteaders were Midwesterners. Some were second- and third-generation Americans; others were of German, Scandinavian, Russian, or other European stock. Daniel Freeman, the first man to file his claim for land under the Homestead Act, was an Illinois farmer. After the Civil War ended, Freeman settled on his 160-acre quarter section which was near the town of Beatrice, Nebraska.

Oklahoma, the very last of the plains states to be homesteaded, had been set aside in the early part of the century as Indian territory, to house those tribes that had been removed from the more thickly settled Southern states. Then, precisely at noon on April 22, 1889, unassigned land in the central part of the territory was opened for white settlement. The rush was on! By covered wagon, by carriage, by cart, on foot, and on horseback, land-hungry pioneers dashed into the territory to stake their claims. One man was even said to have ridden an ostrich! In a few days' time, the remaining good farm lands in the United States had been spoken for— and the last frontier was no more.

Pioneer life on the plains had its special problems. The absence of trees meant that there was no wood available for building or for fuel. With enterprise, hard work, and great good humor, the pioneers came up with "Nebraska marble," large thick chunks of sod cut into rectangular blocks and stacked one atop the other to build the cabin walls. Floors were of hard-packed earth, and roofs were made up of more sod supported by poles and rafters taken from a precious few trees that grew near a distant river bank.

Some of the sod houses of the plains were really dugouts,

built into the earth wall of an embankment and requiring
only a front and a partial roof of sod. But most of the permanent homes were four-wall "soddies." The "permanence"
of a sod house was, however, restricted to an average life of
six or seven years. After that it had to be rebuilt, hopefully
with lumber hauled from the East.

While the sun-baked blocks of earth, grass, and roots were
good insulators, warm in winter and cool in summer, they
offered housing that was far from luxurious—and was often
downright uncomfortable. Dirt and bugs tended to sift down
from the ceilings in dry weather, mice were everywhere, and
in rainy weather the sod houses were prone to leak. Grass and
even flowers grew out of the sod roof, but this picturesque
aspect had its disadvantages, for sometimes cows wandered
onto the roofs of dugout houses in search of grazing land,
and ended up in the one-room interior below.

With trees so scarce on the plains, the use of wood for
heating and cooking fuel was unthinkable. Even window
frames and door frames were usually made out of old boxes,
and a stout piece of leather or canvas served for the door
itself. The homesteaders, therefore, turned to the fuel of the
plains Indians—dried buffalo chips. As the number of domes-

tic animals increased, dried cow dung came into use, and
once the first cornfields had been planted and reaped, the
homesteaders burned dried cornstalks and corncobs in the
fireplaces of their sod dwellings. Dried grass, hay, and weeds
could also be burned, and special stoves were designed for
the purpose, but these fuels were very dangerous.

The lack of both wood and metal on the plains meant that
farm implements, tools of every sort, cooking utensils, and
even the smallest item of tableware had to be brought along
from a former household. Woe to the unprepared and the
ill-provided, for the inhospitable plains demanded thrift,
industry, and ingenuity from those who wished to survive.

The scarcity of accessible water was another serious problem. Not all homesteads were situated near a stream or other
watercourse, and lack of rainfall made such sources unre-
liable anyway. Wells had to be dug, and fortunately these
revealed that the land was almost everywhere underlaid with

water, although at a considerable depth. Wells on the plains often went down 300 feet, and because hand pumping was laborious, the winds of the plains were at last harnessed to a useful purpose. Typical of the plains' landscape of the late 1800s were the tall twirling windmills of the widely scattered homesteads.

An important contribution to the agriculture of the plains was made by a group of German Mennonites who had for some time been living in Russia. In the 1870s they immigrated to Kansas to buy inexpensive lands offered for sale by the newly built railroads. With them, the newcomers brought a variety of winter wheat known as Turkey red, which proved itself admirably suited to cultivation in this region of the New World and helped to make Kansas the present-day "breadbasket of America." Nebraska, too, saw the immigration of many German-Russians at this time.

Not all of the railroad land offerings brought such happy results. In an effort to increase their freight traffic, the railroads were not above making fraudulent promises of rich soil, ample rainfall, or quick irrigation schemes. In their stead new settlers often encountered every hardship from buffalo stampedes to droughts, blizzards, and the total destruction of their crops by grasshoppers. Disheartened, many farmers abandoned their holdings, packed their belongings, and headed East. Written on their wagons were the rueful words, "Goin' back to my wife's folks."

For those who hung on, the rewards were slow but steady. In Nebraska the realization that trees were vital as windbreaks, as sources of shelter and fuel, and as a means of conserving moisture led to a forestation program begun by J. Sterling Morton, who later became Secretary of Agriculture under President Cleveland and was responsible for the first Arbor Day, observed in 1872.

The last great struggle of the plains was that between the homesteaders and the cattlemen. With the coming of the railroads, more and more cattle from Texas and the Southwest were being driven across the plains states to railroad points in Kansas and Nebraska for shipment East. These long cattle drives were immensely destructive to the newly planted fields of the homesteaders. The cattlemen, on the other hand, resented the intrusion of the homesteaders who were plowing under the buffalo grass that was feed for their cattle.

The invention of barbed wire in 1874 gave the homesteaders a weapon with which to fence out the marauding herds, and by the 1880s the "open range" was a thing of the past on the Great Plains. Increased productivity through irrigation and proper use of the land led to better living conditions. As the railroads began to ship lumber from the East, the sod houses of the pioneers began to give way to improved wooden farmhouses. The heating and cooking problem, too, was finally solved as coal from the East was brought to the plains states by rail.

FOOD FESTIVALS OF THE MIDWEST AND THE GREAT PLAINS   The cookery of the plains was deeply rooted in that of the Midwest. Strong German and Scandinavian influences were notable too. As in most pioneer communities the early settlers dwelt at considerable distances from one another. But the aching loneliness of frontier life was even more deeply felt across the unchanging vista of the plains. Festive gatherings were few, so that the strawberry social and the Fourth of July picnic were not only eagerly awaited, but became firmly entrenched institutions in the social life of the plains.

In June when the strawberries were ripe and sweet in eastern Kansas, in Nebraska, in Missouri, or almost anywhere throughout the Great Plains or the Midwest, there was sure to be a strawberry social held at the church, schoolhouse, or farmers' co-operative. An entire picnic lunch or supper might be served, but the feature of the occasion was always strawberry shortcake consisting of a rich biscuit-dough shortcake, split and buttered while hot, deluged with crushed sweetened strawberries, and drowned in rich heavy sweet cream.

This luscious concoction is sometimes referred to as old-fashioned strawberry shortcake, but in truth there is no other kind. Spongecake garnished with whipped cream and topped with a few rather lonely-looking strawberries (although it has its merits) would never dare to show up at a *real* old-fashioned strawberry social.

The Fourth of July picnic was the high point of the year, for it came at the beginning of summer and could be celebrated out of doors. Often it took the form of a box social with the young women and girls of the community packing box lunches full of mysterious but wonderful eatables to be passed on to their beaus, or to be auctioned off, sight unseen, to the highest bidder. It was then customary for the young lady who had packed the lunch to join the winning gentleman in the eating of it.

Fried chicken, baked ham, potato salad, deviled eggs, pickled beets, corn relish, home-baked bread, and angel-food or layer cake were almost sure to turn up beneath the careful wrappings at the box social picnic. Watermelon was the indispensable community dessert at all such outdoor gatherings.

Later in the season of outdoor festivities came the corn roast, the fresh green "roastin'" ears cooked in their white inner husks over smoldering hickory fires. Cooked in this fashion, the corn kernels became faintly browned and took on a delightful caramelized flavor. Roasted corn, dripping with butter, was eaten with barbecued pork or fried chicken at roasts stretching across the corn belt into Iowa, and beyond onto the Great Plains.

FOOD PRODUCTS OF THE MIDWEST AND THE GREAT PLAINS TODAY

Wheat and beef; corn and hogs; the great cereal bowl and breadbasket of the nation—all of these phrases characterize the vast heartland of the United States. However, a closer look at this region, state by state, reveals a surprising wealth and variety of food products.

In addition to corn, dairy cattle, and hogs Ohio produces potatoes, soybeans, apples, great quantities of Swiss cheese, and large amounts of Liederkranz and Camembert cheese. On the fringes of Lake Erie and on the offshore islands, the moisture-tempered climate is favorable to the growing of excellent peaches and grapes. A wine industry flourishes in the grape-growing region. Although Cincinnati's meat-packing days belong chiefly to the past, it is interesting to note that in the 1850s this Ohio city was nicknamed Porkopolis, so busy was it with the work of turning Ohio, Indiana, and Kentucky hogs into hams and sausages.

In Indiana the growing of corn is paramount, with wheat and other grains also important. Soybeans and tomatoes are vital crops. There is a large tomato-canning industry in the state. In the "muck" soils of the northern section, spearmint and peppermint are grown. "Muck" soil is one-time swampland, rich in deposits of decayed vegetation.

Illinois leads the states in the production of soybeans and Swiss cheese. Corn growing and livestock raising are highly important, and Chicago, of course, is the nation's leading cattle market and meat-packing center.

Favorable soil and climate conditions on western Michigan's lake shore make this state the leading grower of cherries. Blueberries, plums, and apples have also become important fruit crops in Michigan. Celery, beans, and spearmint are grown extensively. Inland and Great Lakes fisheries send trout, whitefish, carp, lake herring, smelts, perch, and pike to market. Battle Creek is an important cereal-food center, particularly in the manufacture of ready-to-eat varieties.

Wisconsin leads the states in the production of condensed and evaporated milk and cheese of all types, of which it puts forth more than one hundred varieties. On the Lake Michi-

gan shore, cherries are grown, and the marshy areas are an excellent source of cranberries. Apples, too, are an important fruit crop. Milwaukee is a very large brewery center.

Minnesota has been called the "bread and butter" state because of her first-ranking production of butter and her great flour-milling operations, particularly in Minneapolis. This state also ranks first in the production of honey, turkeys, and sweet corn. Wheat, wild rice, potatoes, and the corn- and pea-canning industries play vital roles in Minnesota's economy. Beef as well as dairy cattle are raised, and St. Paul is a top meat-packing center. Minnesota, "the land of ten thousand lakes," actually has more than fourteen thousand lakes, each covering over twenty-five acres! Northern and wall-eyed pike, trout, bass, whitefish, and herring are just a few of the fish caught commercially in these and in Lake Superior waters.

Iowa corn and hogs are famous. The state also produces wheat and soybeans, cattle and poultry, and special food items such as nuts, popcorn, and honey. Apples are an important crop, the famous Red Delicious apple having been developed in Iowa in 1872. Meat packing and cereal milling are thriving Iowa food industries.

Missouri, like Iowa, sends most of its corn to market in the form of hogs. Kansas City is an important slaughtering and meat-packing center. Flour milling is also a vital industry in this city. Missouri produces excellent apples, peaches, strawberries, and watermelons. St. Louis is a large brewing center.

North Dakota's wheat production is second only to that of Kansas. This state leads, however, in the production of spring wheat and durum wheat. Durum is a hard variety of wheat used in making spaghetti and macaroni. South Dakota is also a principal wheat-growing state. Both states also grow rye, barley, potatoes, soybeans, sugar beets, and feed corn. Sheep, hogs, cattle, and poultry, including turkeys, are raised in the Dakotas.

In eastern Nebraska, wheat, corn, and dairy cattle are raised. The western half of the state is grazing land for beef cattle, with the city of Omaha a great meat-packing center.

Flour milling, too, is a leading industry in this city. Potatoes, sugar beets, and soybeans are significant crops.

Kansas, located geographically in the very center of the United States, is the country's leading wheat-growing state. Corn and other grains are also grown, and the state produces apples and apple seedlings, as well as strawberries and other fruits.

Oklahoma yields important crops of wheat, corn, and potatoes. Cattle, sheep, hogs, and poultry are raised. In her southern and eastern portions, Oklahoma grows apples and peaches, as well as pecans and peanuts.

RECIPES OF THE MIDWEST AND THE GREAT PLAINS

MIDWESTERN POTATO SALAD

(3 to 4 servings)

4	medium-sized potatoes
	Salt
	Freshly ground black pepper
½	teaspoon finely diced onions
4	tablespoons mayonnaise
3	tablespoons sour cream
1	tablespoon salad oil
2	tablespoons cider vinegar
½	teaspoon prepared mustard
1	tablespoon finely chopped parsley
⅛	teaspoon celery seed

Pare potatoes, cut into ½- to ¾-inch cubes, and cook in boiling salted water until just tender. Drain and dry well by shaking potatoes in pan over the heat for a few minutes. Sprinkle while still hot with salt, pepper, and onions. Toss lightly and set aside to cool.

In a bowl combine the remaining ingredients. Blend smooth and fold into potatoes gently but thoroughly. Taste and adjust seasonings, adding salt if necessary. Serve chilled, sprinkled with additional parsley. This is a German-style potato salad, excellent with cold cuts or frankfurters.

OLD-FASHIONED STRAWBERRY SHORTCAKE

(4 servings)

1	pint fresh strawberries
2 to 4	tablespoons sugar
1	cup sifted all-purpose flour
1½	teaspoons baking powder
⅛	teaspoon salt
1	tablespoon sugar
3	tablespoons butter or margarine
¼	cup milk

Hull berries, wash, and slice into halves or, if large, into thirds. Add sugar to desired sweetness and set aside while preparing shortcakes.

Sift the flour, baking powder, salt, and 1 tablespoon of sugar into a mixing bowl. Using a pastry blender or two knives crisscrossing, cut in the butter or margarine until the mixture appears crumbly. Add the milk all at once and stir with a fork until a stiff dough is formed. If the mixture seems too dry to gather into a ball, add a few more drops of milk.

Pat or roll the dough out on a floured board or pastry cloth to a thickness of ½ inch. Cut into four rounds, each about 2¾ to 3 inches in diameter. Bake shortcakes on an ungreased baking sheet at 450 degrees for 12 to 15 minutes, or until lightly browned. Split horizontally while still warm, and butter the insides.

To serve, place bottom half of shortcake in a deep dessert dish. Spoon berries and juice over it. Cover with top half of shortcake and add more berries and juice. Pour thick, heavy cream over all, or top with sweetened whipped cream, flavored with vanilla.

THE SOUTHWEST

Texas

New Mexico

Arizona

THE PUEBLO INDIANS, the Spanish, the Mexicans, and the American cowboy have all contributed to the unique flavor of Southwestern cookery. From the humble bean-and-corn-meal diet of the native Indian to the lavish Texas beef barbecue of modern times, Southwestern cuisine is strongly bound up with the procession of peoples who settled this region—and with the land itself.

A first look at the arid sun-baked plateaus of the Southwest, at its gorges and precipices, its steep-sided mesas and towering buttes, makes one wonder at the ability of such a landscape to support human life. Indeed much of the Southwest is true desert, parched and treeless, covered with whirling sands.

The likeness of these desert areas to those of Asia and of North Africa was, in fact, so great that in the 1850s the United States Government actually undertook to import camels from abroad. The camels were to be used as pack animals for army posts located in the barren wastes of the Southwest. But horses stampeded at the sight of these strange beasts, and the gravelly sands and spiny vegetation of the American desert were hard on the camels' hoofs. The experiment was therefore abandoned and the camels were turned loose and eventually shot.

The Southwest really begins somewhere in Texas. However, this largest of the first forty-eight states is so sprawling that she encompasses characteristics of both the South and the Great Plains within her borders. Eastern Texas is rice-

growing coastal plain, its low marshy shoreline skirting the
Gulf of Mexico. Northern Texas, particularly in the Panhandle, is wheat-growing country and belongs geographically
to the Great Plains that extend northward to Canada.

Stretching westward from central Texas, across New Mexico and into Arizona, is the true Southwest—the land of the
stiff-armed cactus, the creamy-flowered yucca, and the mesquite, a shrublike tree that grows even under conditions of
extreme dryness. Here, too, are the Grand Canyon, the Petri-
fied Forest, and the Painted Desert, for this is one of the
most richly scenic regions in the world.

THE INDIAN VILLAGES OF THE SOUTHWEST

Oddly enough, the Indian tribes of the treeless and water-
less Southwest were predominantly farmers. They grew more
maize than the Indians of the eastern woodlands. They grew
squash, beans, melons, and pumpkins as well, and unlike
other agricultural tribes, it was the men rather than the
women who tended the fields, and even spun and wove
cloth from the wild cotton that grew in their semidesert
habitat.

Hunting was a secondary and little-practiced occupation
for the men of the tribes. Meat was sometimes obtained by
trading with neighboring tribes who made hunting expeditions onto the Great Plains for buffalo. Nearer to home there
were mountain lions, deer, antelope, and bears. But the agricultural villages of the Southwest frequently contented themselves with rabbit and with the one-time wild turkey, which
they had domesticated.

When the Spanish first explored this region they gave the
inhabitants of these agricultural Indian communities the
name of Pueblo (meaning "town" or "village"). The civilization of the Pueblo Indians was a very old one which had
reached its peak of development three hundred years earlier,
about 1200. At that time the Pueblos lived in huge cliff
apartment houses and in multi-storied terraced fortresses, the
rooms of each numbering in the hundreds. Prolonged periods

of drought, or perhaps repeated raids by the nomadic Apache and Navaho tribes, finally drove these apartment dwellers to abandon their great clustered cities and to build smaller, scattered villages near more dependable sources of water.

Many of the Indian villages that the Spanish found are still in existence today, their fields primitively irrigated, their corn ground into meal by hand between rough stones. Bread is still baked in the outdoor dome-shaped beehive ovens that are so characteristic of all Pueblo villages. The fire is generally built of brush. When the oven is properly heated, the embers are swept out and the corn bread is put in to bake, with a sheepskin flap drawn over the opening to retain the oven heat. The Hopi, Zuñi, Tano, Pima, and Papago are some of the Pueblo tribes that have remained aloof from modern civilization and still retain their old way of life in parts of Arizona and New Mexico.

Very different from the peaceable field-tending Indians of the Pueblo tribes were the roving Apaches, Navahos, Comanches, and Utes of the Southwestern plains. These tribes practiced no agriculture and were chiefly hunters and raiders. While the Pueblo Indians built their homes of adobe, or sun-baked clay, or of stone, to serve as permanent dwellings, the Apaches lived in rude brush huts or in tepees. The Navahos preferred the hogan, a cone or dome-shaped shelter of logs, brush, and mud.

All of these nomadic tribes were quick to acquire horses once the Spanish had introduced these animals to the New World. They became excellent horsemen, intensifying their raiding activities and terrorizing the Pueblo villages and the Spanish and Mexican outposts as well. Their object was usually more horses. They also took cattle, sheep, mules. prisoners and, quite often, scalps. It is believed that the Navahos learned the art of weaving from Pueblo Indians whom they captured, for they eventually became sheepherders and master weavers, and settled down to a much more peaceable existence in the semidesert of northeastern Arizona, which they still occupy today.

The foods of the marauding tribes of the Southwest were limited to game, whatever corn or other agricultural products they were able to obtain from the Pueblos, and wild fruits, berries, and nuts.

The fruit of the prickly-pear cactus, a plant fairly common in the Southwest, was also known in some areas as the Indian fig. The bumpy-skinned prickly pear, which grows at the tips of paddle-shaped cactus leaves, resembles a thick shortened cucumber. Its skin color ranges from dull green to purple, but its pulp is a vivid purplish red. Although juicy and fairly sweet, the flesh of the prickly pear is mottled with small hard seeds. In modern times, the pulp is puréed for use in jellies and candies.

The beans of the wild mesquite were used by the Indians for food, as were the flat oval seeds of the stunted low-growing piñon pine, often called pine nuts. From the mesquite bean the Indians of the Southwest prepared a stone-ground flour which they mixed with water to form a dough, shaped into little cakes, and baked in the sun until very dry. These were known as mesquite bean cakes, and are still eaten today in Indian villages along with coffee or milk.

Pinole is another ancient Indian dish prepared with dried maize, mesquite beans, and other parched grains or seeds. Jerky was, of course, a favorite way of preserving venison or other meat in the Southwest, with the hot sun serving as a perfect drying agent. A jerky stew was made by pounding the dried meat to bits and boiling it in water to which a little corn meal was added. It was served with Indian *tortillas,* round thin cakes of corn meal and water.

While the foods of the Southwestern Indians may seem dull, bland, and even downright unappetizing to us, they were the perfect base for the piquant, flavorful, and succulent embellishments introduced by the Spanish—garlic, olives, onions, peppers, tomatoes, *chorizo* (Spanish pork sausage), citrus fruits, apricots, and numerous others that have made Southwestern cooking the attractive cuisine it is today.

Nearly seventy years before the English made their first New World settlement at Jamestown, the Spanish, having traveled northward from Mexico, were exploring the American Southwest. Behind them lay the conquered lands of the Inca and the Aztec.

THE CULINARY GIFTS OF THE SPANISH CONQUERORS

As a result of their exploits in South and Central America, in Mexico, and in the West Indies, the Spanish had already introduced to Europe the potato (both white and sweet), the tomato, the cacao bean, the vanilla bean, several varieties of peppers, and the native American turkey. These foods were, on the whole, well received in Europe, and the Spanish, combining the South American tomato with their native olive oil, onions, garlic, and spices, came up with the first tomato sauce. (The tomato, which traveled on to Italy, found special favor there, for it was just what was needed to complement the spaghetti that Marco Polo had brought back from China.)

Most of the foods that the Spanish took home from the tropical and semitropical Americas were to be introduced into North America at a later date. In this sense they acted as purveyors, or carriers, of world foodstuffs. But even more important were the livestock, fruits, vegetables, nuts, grains, herbs, and spices that the Spanish brought to the New World *directly* from Europe.

By about 1609 the Spanish had established the mission fortress of Santa Fe in what is now New Mexico, making this capital city the oldest seat of government in the United States. Only St. Augustine in Florida is older as a city surviving from an original colonization.

During the next two hundred years Spanish priests were to found missions throughout the Southwest, as far east as Texas, and as far north and west as Sonoma, California, north of San Francisco. The attempt to bring Christianity to the Pueblo Indians met with revolt in some quarters, but many Indians of the Southwest accepted life as workers on the mission farms. In return the padres offered them Christian teachings and saw to their welfare.

At first only Indian corn, beans, and squash, plus wheat, rice and some garden produce introduced by the Spanish were grown on the mission farms. Later mission agriculture yielded groves of citrus fruits, vineyards, walnut, almond, and olive trees, and fruits such as avocados, apricots, and pears. Much of the present agricultural wealth of California is due to the influence of the Spanish missions and their patient Indian labor.

Cattle, sheep, goats, and fowl were raised on the mission farms, but the true stock raisers were the wealthy Spanish cattlemen who were the *patróns* (landlords) of large ranches worked by Mexicans and Indians. The Mexicans who herded cattle for the Spanish were the first cowboys of the Southwest, and are said to have taught the colorful American cowboy his skills.

Surely the most picturesque livestock of the old Southwest were the longhorn cattle, descendants of Andalusian cattle brought to Mexico from Spain as early as the 1520s. It is quite true, however, that the longhorns of the Southwest were not choice beef cattle. They were often tough and stringy, and their meat had a gamy quality. Aside from a few tender morsels, they were raised largely for their hides and tallow.

Later, in the 1860s, when Texas longhorns began to be shipped east via the newly built railroads, they sold at low prices. Their meat, ground and spiced, was used chiefly for home-style sausages by the Polish, Hungarian, German, and Italian immigrant populations of cities like Chicago, St. Louis, and Cincinnati. The tradition of using ground beef or small cubes of beef in stews is still seen in many Southwestern dishes such as *albondigas* soup (a Mexican tomato-and-beef broth with tiny meat balls) and *chili con carne* (chili with meat, a stew of diced beef cooked with onions, garlic, chili powder, and red beans).

"Western beef" continued to be poorly thought of until shorthorns and Herefords (both cattle of English origin) from eastern herds were moved west, and the breeding stock was improved. Nevertheless, the sale of hides, many of which were shipped to New England shoe factories, made the raising of longhorn cattle profitable for many years in the Southwest.

MEXICAN COOKING IN THE AMERICAN SOUTHWEST

When we speak of Mexican cooking, we really mean the Spanish-Indian dishes that developed in the land of the Aztecs beginning with the Spanish conquest of 1519. From those early years until some years after Mexico won her independence from Spain in 1821, Texas, New Mexico, and Arizona were all a part of Mexico. It is not surprising, therefore, that the cookery of this region, with its heavy Mexican population, should be deeply rooted in that of its neighbor to the south.

Tortillas and *frijoles* (beans, either pink, red, black, or the spotted pinto variety) are the two most basic foods of the Mexican peasant. The translation of the word *tortilla* is really "little cake." To prepare tortillas, dried corn is cooked in a solution of lime and water until it is tender. The Mexican peasant woman then grinds the wet kernels on a flat stone called a *metate*. The smooth doughy mass that results is known as *masa*. In larger Mexican cities and in many Southwestern towns, *masa* is prepared commercially and may be purchased ready to use. Mexican women are skilled at shaping small chunks of *masa* dough into large, thin wafer-like rounds, then toasting these on a big flat pan over the fire. The resulting pale brown cakes are the tortillas.

In its simplest form, the tortilla is used as a spoon to dip up the boiled black beans that are eaten as often as three times a day by the poor of Mexico. A little roasted chili pepper provides the seasoning for this bland combination. But tortillas can go much farther than this. They are to the Mexican what bread is to other peoples of the world.

A slice of bread may be eaten plain, toasted, or fried. It may be used as the basis for a hot or cold open sandwich, or combined with a second slice of bread and layered with almost any sandwich filling. So it goes with the tortilla.

The *enchilada,* for example, is a tortilla fried in fat until it is hot but still flexible. It is then dipped in hot chili pepper sauce and sprinkled with such tasty items as grated cheese, chopped onions, chopped green olives, or what have you. The tortilla is then rolled up, splashed with more hot sauce, and topped with more filling. Shredded lettuce is often added to the topping.

To make *tacos,* tortillas are folded in half and fried crisp, then filled with beans, cheese, vegetables, chopped meats or poultry, alone or in combination. Sometimes the taco is filled first, fastened into a turnover, and then fried. The taco is really the closed sandwich of the tortilla family.

The *tostada* is again a tortilla, this time fried flat and heaped high with such savory things as Mexican sausage, beans, grated cheese, or chopped meats. Shredded lettuce and minced onion are popular garnishes which are inserted into the opening of the taco or sprinkled atop the tostada.

In the American Southwest all of these extended uses of the tortilla may be sampled, and there are almost endless variations on the basic themes described.

Tamales (a single one is a tamal) are distantly related to the tortilla family, but related they are, for their basic ingredient is again corn meal. The word *tamal* really means "bundle," which is a good description of this Mexican-style dumpling. The Mexican farm family saves dried cornhusks from its harvested corn for use in making tamales. The husks are softened in water until pliable, then spread with a layer of cereal paste made of *masa* or corn meal mixed with lard, salt, and broth. A well-seasoned pork, chicken, or other filling is dabbed atop the cereal paste, and the tamal is rolled up lengthwise. Tamales are usually tied, with additional strips of cornhusk, into bundles of six. They are cooked by steaming over boiling water in a tightly covered kettle.

A Southwestern variation of the tamale is tamale pie, a cooked mixture of chopped beef, onions, green pepper, and tomatoes seasoned with chili powder and spooned into a casserole atop a layer of corn-meal mush. Another layer of corn meal tops the meat mixture and the dish is slowly baked to a steaming golden goodness.

Frijoles are almost as important as corn in Mexican and Southwestern cookery. They are used in soups, in meat stews (such as chili con carne), in chicken dishes, as fillings for tacos and other tortilla variations, and as *frijoles refritos* (refried beans). In this popular dish beans are cooked in water until tender, then mashed and fried in hot fat until they are crispy around the edges. Garlic, chili powder, and salt are used as seasonings. *Frijoles fritos* (fried beans) are cooked beans which are then mashed with bean liquid and lightly fried in fat to a thick, but not crisp, mush.

Garbanzos, or chick-peas (the same legume found in the Spanish cookery of St. Augustine, Florida), are used in Mexican soups and other dishes. Rice, too, which was introduced by the Spanish, is a much-used ingredient, a favorite in soups and in *arroz con pollo* (rice with chicken). This dish of golden chicken pieces browned in garlic-seasoned olive oil and simmered in a broth of rice, herbs, and seasonings, is Spanish in origin. Saffron (a yellow flavoring obtained from the stigmas of the crocus flower), crimson pimento, and green peas give glamorous color to this excellent recipe, now popular in both Mexico and the American Southwest.

Distinctly Aztec in origin is turkey *mole* (pronounced

mo-lay) which goes back to pre-Hispanic times in Mexico and is said to have been served to the Spanish conqueror, Cortez, by Montezuma, the Aztec emperor. If the *mole* sauce for the turkey is to be made properly it requires as many as twenty-eight different ingredients, one of which is always bitter chocolate. While chocolate may seem an odd flavoring in a sauce to be served with poultry, it must be remembered that *mole* is not in the least like the chocolate sauce we use with ice cream and other desserts. *Mole* contains only enough ground chocolate to add a touch of pungency, and lists among its other ingredients several kinds of chili peppers, almonds, raisins, peanuts, cinnamon, cloves, and dry bread or toast. These ingredients are ground together and combined with onions, garlic, herbs and additional spices, as well as tomatoes, and turkey or chicken broth.

The salad favorite of Mexican and Southwestern cuisine is the avocado, sometimes called the alligator pear. This fruit with its dark green to purplish skin and its pale buttery flesh grows wild in tropical America and is therefore native to certain regions of Mexico. It is also cultivated in modern times in California and Florida.

The mixture made by combining mashed avocado with onion, garlic, chili peppers, and tomato is called *guacamole*. It may be served as a salad course, and has become highly popular in California and the Southwest as an appetizer dip to be spread on crackers or other crisp base.

Chocolate, which is derived from the cacao bean native to Mexico, makes a favorite beverage in that country. Mexican chocolate is prepared by cooking the chocolate with water and flavoring it with cinnamon. It is beaten to a foam with a wooden beater. Across the border, in the United States, this drink is likely to be enriched by the addition of milk. Ground coffee is sometimes added for stronger flavor.

Desserts in Mexico and the Southwest often consist of fresh fruits, including many semitropical varieties. Sweet puddings, sometimes molded and chilled, prepared with dates, walnuts, mashed yams or sweet potatoes, or candied mixed fruits, are also popular.

THE AMERICAN COWBOY AND THE CHUCKWAGON

The first Americans began to drift into Texas in the 1820s. At about the same time, the Santa Fe Trail—which ran from Independence, Missouri, to Santa Fe, New Mexico—began to see wagon traffic. However, the wagon trains that made the perilous 850-mile journey in those early years came to Santa Fe chiefly for trade, bringing much-needed goods from the East to the Spanish-American landowners, and taking in return silver and furs.

Settlement by Americans from the East was slow at first in New Mexico. It was hastened somewhat after the Mexican War in 1848 when Mexico ceded her large holdings in the Southwest to the United States. The following year stagecoach service was established on the Santa Fe Trail. The trip from Independence took two weeks, and the fare, with no guarantees against Indian warfare and other hazards, cost two hundred fifty dollars, an enormous amount of money for those days.

In Arizona, settlement was even more tardy due to the lack of transportation facilities into the region. Copper, silver, and gold mining, which were developed in the 1850s, finally spurred American settlement. Not until 1912, however, did either New Mexico or Arizona have a large enough population to qualify for admission to the Union.

The most colorful culinary contribution of the Americans of the Southwest is surely the chuckwagon. This rolling kitchen came into use in the 1860s when the first long cattle drives from Texas to the newly built Kansas railheads got under way. The herds of longhorns, sometimes numbering as many as three thousand, were not hurried on their six- or seven-hundred-mile journey to the depot, for it was discovered that the animals fattened wonderfully as they fed on the grasses of northern Texas, Oklahoma, and Kansas.

Weeks often stretched into months on the long summer drives, which followed the yearly spring roundup. During this time three substantial meals a day had to be provided for the dozen or so cowboys and the trail boss who made up the typical trail outfit.

The invention of the chuckwagon is credited to Colonel Charles Goodnight, a pioneer cattleman of the Texas Panhandle. Actually a chuckwagon was just an ordinary wagon that had a tall box with a drop door built onto the back of it. The box was a traveling pantry containing shelves that held flour, corn meal, salt, coffee, brown sugar, dried pinto beans, lard, bacon, salt pork, raisins, and whatever other staples might be needed. The chuckwagon generally carried enough provisions to last two months.

When the wagon was traveling, the drop door covered the pantry shelves and kept things from tumbling about. When the outfit came to a halt, the door was let down, and by means of two hinged legs, converted into a table. Here the cook, sometimes called "cookie," sometimes "pot wrangler," prepared the food for the trail outfit. If the food was not to the liking of the men, he might be called other names considerably less flattering, but in any case the trail cook was in a position of authority and the chuckwagon his supreme domain.

In the body of the wagon were kept the skillets, stew pots, and Dutch oven that the cook required, as well as the tin plates and cups, forks, spoons, and knives with which the trail gang ate. A water cask, lashed to the side of the wagon, had to be kept filled and watched carefully in dry country.

Fuel, however, was the greatest problem of the chuckwagon boss. Wood and twigs were gathered continually along the way to be stored in a cowhide slung across the underbody of the wagon. When wood ran out, there was no choice but to gather and burn cow chips. But these were truly a last resort, for they gave an unpleasant odor and burned much too quickly.

One of the most important staples of the chuckwagon pantry was a firkin, or small wooden cask, of sourdough "starter," which was used in making biscuits and hotcakes. The sourdough was a fermented mixture of flour, salt, and water to which sugar, molasses, or boiled mashed potatoes had been added to speed the fermentation, or "souring." Sourdough was used for leavening baked goods, and took the place of yeast or baking powder, neither of which was available in early chuckwagon days.

The important thing was to keep the sourdough mixture warm enough so that fermentation could continue. On cold nights the cook took the firkin of starter to bed with him, for extremes of temperature could kill its action and ruin his biscuits for the rest of the cattle drive. When making biscuits, the cook simply took a blob of sourdough from his starter mixture and worked it into his biscuit dough. At the same time he added enough flour, lukewarm water, and salt to the firkin to replace the amount of starter he had used up. This soon became fermented, and with care a sourdough starter could go on working for years.

The biscuit dough was rolled out and cut into rounds with a lid or an opened tin can. Then the biscuits were set to rise, the sourdough working in them so they would be light and fluffy when baked. Since no baking oven was available on the trail, biscuits were baked in a Dutch oven, a heavy covered iron pot which had been heated over an outdoor fire. Sourdough biscuits tasted best when they were freshly baked and still hot.

Chuckwagon stew was a favorite out on the range. It consisted mostly of tongue, heart, kidneys, liver, brains, and usually something the cowboys called marrow gut. This was a tube connecting the stomachs of a nursing calf, and containing partly digested milk which became a marrowlike substance when cooked. Cowboys were especially fond of it. Some lean meat (usually a piece of tenderloin), onions, chili peppers, and salt were also included in the stew.

Steaks, like stews, were everyday chuckwagon fare. The fresh-meat supply was trotting along right beside the rolling kitchen most of the time, so it is little wonder that meat was eaten three times a day, with steak a standby at breakfast. Steaks were usually salted and floured, then fried on a sizzling skillet in beef suet. This method sealed in the juices and gave the meat a crisp browned coating. Many Easterners look askance at steaks that are fried rather than broiled, but it must be remembered that high-heat broilers were unknown in chuckwagon days and fuel had to be used as sparingly as possible. All cooking, of course, was done over outdoor fires.

Slaughtering was usually done near the close of the day so the meat could be hung in the cool night air of the plains. During the day when the temperature soared, the cooled meat was wrapped in heavy canvas for insulation, and stowed away beneath the bedrolls in the bottom of the wagon. At night the carcass was cooled again, and so on until the meat supply of that kill had been used up. This was the refrigeration system of the trail.

If the members of the trail gang tired of beef, there was almost always game to be had for the shooting—venison, antelope, wild turkey, prairie chicken, squirrel, and even buffalo. The one thing that was not available was what the cowboy called garden sass. Edible greens were rare on the high, dry plains of the Southwest. Dried beans were the nearest thing to a vegetable that the cowboy ever saw during his months on the trail. These were usually pinto beans cooked with salt pork and seasoned with chili powder, garlic, and onion. Although cowboys ate huge amounts of starchy foods, they expended so much energy in their work that it was rare indeed to see a fat cowboy.

Coffee, served black and without sugar, was a round-the-clock beverage on the trail. Cookie kept a pot of hot coffee sitting over the embers whenever the outfit was camped. It was drunk with meals, before meals, between meals, and throughout the night as the various hands came off watch.

The menu for one meal was likely to be much the same as any other. With your eyes closed, you couldn't tell whether you were having breakfast, noon dinner, or supper. Breakfast was usually fried steak, hot corn bread or biscuits, and coffee. Beans, too, were very likely, for a full day of riding and wrangling required chuck that was sufficiently rib-sticking. Chuck was the word the cowboy used for food, seldom mess or chow.

Desserts were only offered now and then. Sometimes Cookie made a pie with dried fruit; other times he served a chuckwagon dessert called spotted pup, consisting of rice cooked with raisins and sweetened with brown sugar.

By the early 1880s the railroads had come farther west and the homesteaders of the plains had plowed under the buffalo grass and fenced in their holdings which were now planted with wheat. For a few years the cattlemen persisted in driving their cattle north and east, cutting the farmers' barbed wire in a series of skirmishes known as fence-cutting wars. But the open range was on its way out, and with it went the heyday of the chuckwagon.

It should be noted, however, that the chuckwagon continued in use on the vast cattle ranches of the Southwest, becoming more modern and efficient with the passing years and offering a much more varied menu.

FIESTAS OF THE SOUTHWEST   Indian ceremonial dances, Mexican fiestas, and Frontier Day celebrations, rodeos, and stock shows are some of the colorful year-round events of the Southwest. Indian, Mexican, and American pioneer segments of the population are each well represented, with each taking pleasure in the festivities of the others, for as the New Mexican saying goes, "What is shared is doubled."

Where food is concerned, no festivity is more popular in the Southwest than the barbecue, be it in connection with politics, business, civic affairs, or purely social in nature. The word *barbecue* comes from the Spanish *barbacoa,* which is derived from a Haitian word meaning "framework of sticks." It was used to describe an outdoor feast of West Indian origin, for the natives of these islands were in the habit of broiling fish out of doors on rude gridirons, supported by wooden stakes. Later, the Spanish introduced to the West Indian natives the custom of roasting an entire hog, ox, or other animal.

About 1700 the barbecue was brought to North America and became popular on the plantations of the South as a most convenient way of entertaining large numbers of guests under pleasant weather conditions. George Washington is reported to have attended many such affairs.

The Southwest, with its extensive supply of beef and its large sprawling cattle ranches, took the institution of the barbecue for its own from the earliest days of settlement. The barbecue sauce with which the roasting meat is basted or brushed, and which is sometimes served atop the meat, is strongly Mexican in influence. Most barbecue sauces contain tomatoes, chili peppers, garlic, onion, vinegar, oil, spices, and a dash of sugar.

The modern barbecue may be an affair for several thousand people in which the meat is roasted in a pit dug es-

pecially for the occasion, or a backyard supper for four, with the food cooked on a portable charcoal grill. The popularity of outdoor cooking and eating has increased tremendously since the Victorian era when meals were taken behind closed doors in oak-paneled dining rooms. Much of the credit for this pleasant fair-weather pastime in the more northerly regions of our country goes to the traditional ranch barbecue of the American Southwest.

FOOD PRODUCTS OF THE SOUTHWEST TODAY

Texas, the largest of the states next to Alaska, has a remarkably varied output of food products. The raising of beef cattle is, of course, paramount on the dry plains of her southwestern sector. In addition sheep ranching, which goes back to the Spanish mission days, is widespread. The Panhandle is wheat country. Texas also produces rice which is cultivated on the coastal plain of the southeast.

The lands bordering the lower Rio Grande are immensely productive as a result of irrigation. Here citrus fruits—grapefruits, lemons, oranges, tangerines, and kumquats—are grown in abundance, as well as dates, avocados, and other semitropical fruits. Texas has a fine output of watermelons, cantaloupes, strawberries, and peaches.

Pecan groves, developed from the wild pecan trees that were flourishing along Texas streams when the first settlers arrived, today yield an enormous crop. Peanuts, too, are grown in Texas.

From the waters of the Gulf of Mexico on her southeastern shore, Texas sends to market shrimp, oysters, Spanish mackerel, redfish, pompano, and other varieties.

New Mexico's vast tracts of arid and semiarid land are taken up with large sheep and cattle ranches. The sheepherders are mainly Navaho Indians and Basques from the mountainous regions of northern Spain. Where the soil and climate permit, wheat, beans, chili peppers, and peanuts are grown. In the irrigated river valleys honeydews, watermelons, and cantaloupes thrive.

The first white men to undertake soil irrigation in Arizona were the Mormons, who settled there in the 1860s. Since then extensive irrigation projects have produced oranges and grapefruits, dates, grapes, cantaloupes, honeydews, and watermelons, fields of lettuce, and groves of olive trees. In the more arid regions of the state, cattle and sheep raising remain top-ranking enterprises.

CHILI CON CARNE

(5 to 6 servings)

A SOUTHWESTERN
RECIPE TO TRY

1½	tablespoons olive oil
1	clove garlic, mashed or put through garlic press
1	large onion, finely diced
1	pound ground beef
2	cups canned tomatoes, with their liquid
½	6-ounce can tomato paste
1½	teaspoons chili powder
1	teaspoon salt
½	teaspoon oregano
1	bay leaf
1	16-ounce can red chili beans, undrained (about 2 cups)
½	cup pitted small ripe olives

In a large, deep skillet, heat the olive oil and add the garlic and the onions. Fry just until light golden brown. Add the ground beef, crumbling it into small quantities as you do so, and fry it just until it loses its red color. Add the tomatoes, the tomato paste, chili powder, salt, oregano, and bay leaf. Simmer, uncovered, on very low heat for 1 hour.

Add the beans and the olives, and cook, uncovered, at low heat for 30 minutes more. Check seasoning and serve. Chili may also be cooled, refrigerated, and reheated in an earthenware casserole or other baking dish on the following day. Its flavor actually improves on standing.

THE WEST

Montana
Wyoming
Colorado
Idaho
Utah
Nevada
Washington
Oregon
California

THE COOKERY of the West is the most difficult to sum up in a single word or a single dish. Until the 1800s most of the land from the Rockies to the Pacific lay fallow, its vast food resources no more dreamed of than its deposits of gold, silver, copper, and other valuable minerals.

Today in the West there are heritages of Spanish cooking from the California mission days and of Midwestern and even Eastern and Southern cooking from the Oregon Trail days. The cuisines of national groups from all over the world are strongly represented in the West, for in the short space of fifty years this region attracted an immense number and variety of immigrant settlers: Welsh, Cornish, and Yugoslav mine workers; Swedish and Finnish lumberjacks; Chinese railroad workers; Italian, Greek, and Japanese fishermen; and fruit growers and dairy farmers of national backgrounds ranging from Armenian to Swiss.

The bounty of the West in modern times is a source of unceasing wonderment. From her coastal areas and rivers come the largest crabs, the tiniest oysters, and the freshest salmon. The fertile valleys of Oregon and California yield a luscious array of fruits and berries. Colorado produces tender juicy beef and fine lamb; Idaho is the home of a superb mealy-textured baking potato. Yet, not very long ago, the Indians of the Rockies ate little but game, those of the Northwest subsisted on salmon, and the chief food of the California tribes was the acorn. Not one of these groups practiced agriculture.

Why should this have been so, in a region of such rich agricultural potential? One reason appears to be the sharp natural boundaries within the West—rugged mountains that break up the land area isolating one section from another and preventing the rainfall necessary for the growth of crops without irrigation.

The Rocky Mountains rise dramatically from the high, treeless breadth of the Great Plains. The eastern halves of Montana, Wyoming, and Colorado are all plains country, their elevations rising steadily as the foothills of the Rockies are approached. The Rockies soar highest in Colorado, but along the spine of these mountains, running north to south through several states, is an imaginary line called the Continental Divide. The Divide is actually a system of high ridges, points at which the directional flow of water separates naturally, running either westward toward the Pacific, or eastward toward the Mississippi.

But the Rockies are not the only agricultural barriers of this region. West of the Rockies lie great plateaus, many of them arid, and some so dry that they are true desert. Other plateaus in this part of the West are really basins, areas into which flow waters that cannot escape to the sea. Great Salt Lake in Utah is fed by such waters.

Farther west another range of mountains comes into view. In California these are called the Sierra Nevadas; farther north in Oregon and Washington they are the Cascades. The western slopes of these mountains, fed by rainfall from the Pacific Ocean, are well forested, and at their base lie the most productive growing valleys of the West. These valleys are, in turn, walled in from the sea by the ridges and spurs of still another chain of mountains, the Pacific Coast Range. In California, even in the fertile soil of the Great Valley, many areas require artificial irrigation because they are so hemmed in by mountain barriers that check their supply of moisture.

More tall tales about natural phenomena have originated in the West than any place else in the United States, and little wonder. The second saltiest body of water on earth in Utah; glaciers that one can reach out and touch in Mon-

tana; a lake that sits in the collapsed crater of a massive vol-
cano in Oregon; and the jet-stream geysers and bubbling
mud pots of Wyoming's Yellowstone Park—all of these have
inspired amazement and understandable elaboration.

The West, too, is a land of extremes, of dramatic contrasts.
California's Mount Whitney is the highest point in the first
forty-eight states, while her Death Valley (at some 280 feet
below sea level) is the lowest. Yet the two lie within 84 miles
of each other. The coastal areas of Washington and Oregon
receive the heaviest rainfall in the United States, while the
deserts of Nevada are among the driest regions in the
country.

Thus physical barriers kept the Indian tribes of the West
very much isolated from one another, while limitations of
climate kept them from realizing the full potential of their
lands.

Between the Rockies and the Sierra Nevadas lived a number
of Indian tribes, most of whom led a wandering life, hunting, fishing occasionally in mountain streams, and gathering seeds and berries or digging for roots. Many were related
to the buffalo hunters of the Great Plains that lay to the
east; some had themselves been buffalo hunters until they
were pushed westward toward the Rockies and beyond.

FOODS OF THE INDIANS OF THE WEST

Game in the Rocky Mountain area was generally plentiful—deer, elk, moose, bear, and the wild bighorn sheep that
frequented the crags and pinnacles of the higher elevations.
Smaller animals were abundant and the lakes and streams
offered good fishing for whitefish, perch, sunfish, and the
famous cutthroat trout, so named because of the slashlike
red markings around its throat. Yellowstone Lake, now part
of Yellowstone National Park, and Jackson Lake, now included in Grand Teton National Park, were among the
largest and most rewarding fishing areas.

Farther west, however, in the plateau country, only smaller
game was generally available and wild plant food was more
limited. The buffalo was not much in evidence west of the
Rockies, for his natural habitat was grassland of the kind
that was abundant only to the east of these mountains.

Some of the tribes of this region between the Rockies
and the Sierras were the Shoshones, the Snakes, the Kiowas,
and the Utes. Most of these Indians came into possession
of horses during the 1700s and carried out raiding activities
against other tribes, particularly those to the south of them.
One of these same tribes, however, probably the Snake or
the Shoshone, was responsible for the famous Indian woman,
Sacajawea, who guided the Lewis and Clark expedition
through the most difficult part of its journey from the Dakota country to the Pacific.

The coastal regions of the Northwest, in what are now
the states of Washington and Oregon, were the home of the
salmon fishermen. In this lush country of much rainfall,
edible fruits and berries, rivers leaping with salmon, we
can hardly blame the Indians for not attempting agriculture.

The Chinooks and other tribes who dwelt at the mouth
of the Columbia River were remarkably experienced in
foretelling the exact time, almost to the hour, of the coming
of the salmon. Spring or fall was the spawning season, with
swarms of the great silvery fish crowding the rivers and
streams as they hurled themselves inland from the sea to
lay their eggs. So heavy were the runs that fishing was easy
for the Indians, sometimes a matter of spearing the salmon
from canoes or from the river bank, or even of clubbing

them to death and scooping them from the water as they passed.

The catch, of course, had to be preserved for almost year-round use. For this purpose the fish was cut into thin strips and dried over the heat of the fire, very much as buffalo and venison were dried to make jerky. The salmon-fishing Indians made a kind of pemmican, too, using fish instead of meat. To prepare this food they pulverized the dried fish almost to a powder, mixed it with berries and perhaps a little flour made by pounding dried roots. Then they stored the mixture in animal skins or in tightly woven baskets.

Salmon eggs and herring eggs were also important in the diet of the Northwestern Indians. To obtain this delicate food the Indians cleverly laid trays or hammocks, made of branches, underwater at shallow places, holding them down with weights. When the trays were found to be covered with eggs they were carefully lifted from the water. Fish eggs that were not eaten immediately were dried, like other

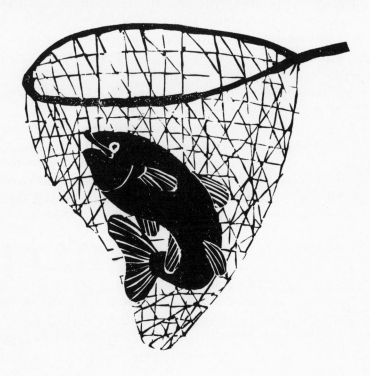

foods, and stored. Shellfish such as oysters, clams, and crabs were also food for the coastal Indians of the Pacific Northwest.

A little farther inland, east of the Cascades, dwelt the Nez Percés, the Yakima, the Wallawalla, and other tribes of the plains and river valleys. Although not so rich in food resources as the coastal area, the streams and rivers of eastern Washington, particularly the Columbia and its tributaries, supplied the Indians with good quantities of salmon and other fish. Small game was also available. Root digging was a popular method of obtaining food among these Indians. The bulb of the camass, a plant related to the lily, was eaten roasted or pounded into meal and used as a kind of flour in breadmaking and in stews. Bitterroot and wild carrot were other edible roots. Wild berries, wild sunflower seeds, and pine nuts rounded out the food supply of these Indians, and in time of real hardship they ate lichens and mosses and even the inner bark of trees. No plant food, however, was cultivated.

In great contrast to their Pueblo neighbors in Arizona and New Mexico were the extremely primitive tribes of Nevada and California. Unlike the agricultural Pueblos, with whom they appear to have had no contact, these Indians ate whatever they happened upon: grasshoppers, roots, wild grass seeds, small game and, most of all, acorns.

The Digger Indians were so named by early white visitors to the semideserts of Nevada and adjoining Utah and California because these Indians were frequently seen grubbing for roots among the sparse vegetation of their land. Antelopes occasionally bounded through this region, but small game and insects were the chief supplements to the root diet of these Indians.

One account by a traveler to California in the early 1840s tells of coming upon a marshy area grown thickly with tule, a kind of bulrush. The surfaces of the rushes were covered with a sweet secretion known as honeydew, and this sticky substance was in turn covered with tiny crawling insects. The Indians gathered the "honey," insects and all, into balls the size of their fists and relished this food, despite (or per-

haps because of) the crunchy texture of the insects pressed
into the mass.

Expending so much effort upon keeping themselves from
starvation, the Diggers had little time for war or for the
development of elaborate ceremonials. They led a crude,
simple life, their homes consisting of mere brush or tule
shelters, often designed as windbreaks. They were scorned
by neighboring tribes, and were sometimes referred to as
Walkers by the proud horse Indians to the north and to the
east of them.

The entire central region of California was occupied by
the acorn-eating Miwok, Maidu, Pomo, Hupa, and other
primitive tribes. Although they practiced no agriculture,
these people had a well-developed economy based on the
storage and processing of the acorn, the single-seeded nut of
the oak tree.

It is not difficult to understand that a people driven by
hunger might be tempted to try almost anything once. So
it must have been with the ancestors of these California
tribes. But the acorn seed, once pressed from its woody cup,
tastes bitter due to the presence of tannic acid, a substance
that is poisonous if taken in large quantities. Nevertheless,
the Indians persisted and eventually succeeded in turning a
bitter puckery nut into a fine bland-tasting yellow meal, an
all-purpose flour and the basis of their daily bread.

Since acorns ripened once a year, harvesting was a major
operation, with the entire tribe repairing to the forest to
climb trees, knock down acorns, gather them, and store them
in the specially woven brush shelters that were used as gran-
aries. The preparation of the nuts was the women's respon-
sibility. They hulled the acorns by setting them on their
ends on grooved stones and pressing down on them with a
hammer stone to release the kernel. Next they had to pound
the acorns with a stone mortar and pestle or similar device,
an almost ceaseless task.

When the meal was fine enough it had to be washed clean
of its bitter and poisonous tannic acid. The women dug a
large saucer-shaped hole in the sand, lining it with the meal
which had been worked into a plasterlike dough. Then they

poured hot water upon the dough again and again, to seep through the meal taking a little more of the bitterness with it each time. The Indian women used the taste test to decide when the acorn dough was sweet enough to be molded into loaves or cakes and baked at the open fire.

For stews, the acorn meal (along with chunks of rabbit or venison, and perhaps a sprig of wild greens) was dropped into a tightly woven basket of water and cooked by the stone-boiling method. The process of boiling water by adding red-hot stones to it was practiced by nearly all the Pacific coast tribes, although it was slow and tedious. It meant that a woman had to sit before her dinner pot nearly all day, re-moving the cooled stones from the water and adding hot ones from the fire to keep the meal at a boil.

The California Indians made no pottery, but their bas-ketry was of a very high quality, both beautiful in design and so densely and precisely woven as to be virtually waterproof, and thus suitable for use as cooking vessels. Like the buf-falo hunters who used an animal skin carefully laid into a hole in the ground as a cooking pot, the Basket Makers often dug a hole in the sand in which to place their cooking basket. Both, of course, used the stone-boiling method. Even after white traders had presented these stone-boiling Indians of the West with flameproof iron cooking pots, they went right on boiling food in them by their ancient method of adding hot stones to the water.

COOKING ALONG
THE OREGON TRAIL

The Oregon Territory first began to attract American set-tlers in the early 1840s. Much larger than the present state of Oregon, this region (which went by the name of "Old Oregon" or simply "the Oregon country") stretched from the northern boundary of California to Alaska. It took in what are now the states of Oregon, Washington, and Idaho, parts of Montana and Wyoming, and also British Columbia.

The Lewis and Clark expedition of 1805, the fur trappers and traders that followed, and a group of American missionaries of the 1830s, all helped to popularize this region of good climate, deep forests, fertile farmlands, and rivers alive with salmon.

In towns along the Missouri River such as Independence, St. Joseph, and Council Bluffs, the prairie schooners gathered to prepare for the two-thousand-mile journey of several months' duration. Each day newcomers arrived from the Midwest, the South, and even the East, and at last when the spring grass on the plains was high enough to afford grazing for their livestock, the wagons set forth.

Each family brought along staples such as flour, corn meal, sugar, coffee, dried beans, rice, bacon, and salt pork. Dried pumpkins, raisins, and dried orchard fruits such as apples and peaches graced the wagon larders of some. The first part of the journey took the wagon trains through Nebraska along the Platte River. Here on the Great Plains buffalo were numerous, almost to the point of danger. Travelers of the time wrote of seeing the plains "black with them for several days' journey as far as the eye could reach."

The Platte drew the buffalo in hordes, especially in spring when they came northward, plunging into the river until the water was discolored and vile to the taste. But the buffalo were also a source of fresh meat to the pioneers during this phase of their travel. A hunting party usually set out on horseback in the morning, returning to the slowly moving wagon train at noon with freshly slaughtered buffalo.

In early spring buffalo meat was lean and stringy, for the animals needed the season of grazing ahead in order to fatten up after the long winter. But the pioneers, with so many men, women, and children to feed, could not afford to be choosy. While mountain men and other loners and small groups of hunters generally took only the tongues, humps, and marrow of the buffalo, leaving the rest for the wolves and the coyotes, the wagon folk soon learned to eat nearly all the ribs and the haunches, too. Young bull buffalo tasted a little coarse, about like middle-grade beef, but the older animals were just plain tough.

A day on the Oregon Trail started at about 4:00 A.M., for the wagon train had to be breakfasted and on its way by daybreak. Beans or corn-meal mush, johnnycake or pancakes, and coffee was the usual breakfast. Fresh milk was available from the dairy cows that most families brought along, and butter could be churned en route.

"Nooning" was the term given to the trail practice of stopping at midday for a meal and a brief rest. Since the daylight hours were important for traveling, only a little time could be spent on the preparation of this meal. If freshly killed buffalo meat was on hand, the more tender cuts were fried for noon dinner, and the stewing or roasting parts left for evening.

At night the caravan camped in a circle or hollow square, the wagons linked tongue to tail or slightly overlapping, to form a barricade against marauding Indians. In dangerous country, fires could not be lit after dark, and supper then consisted of little more than some cold biscuit or johnnycake. Occasionally, however, the entire caravan halted in some pleasant and comparatively safe spot for a day in order to jerk buffalo meat, make minor repairs on the wagons, and attend to the livestock. Children went forth to pick berries or wild greens, if available, for these fresh foods were always a delight to the palate used to a daily diet of beans, bread, and meat.

Fuel varied with the passing countryside, as did water. On the plains where wood was scarce, the wagon folk used buffalo chips for fuel more often than not. Later, in the dry plateau country beyond the Rockies, wood was gathered whenever possible, but since stands of trees were few, sagebrush, tumbleweed, and even dry grass were burned for cooking fuel.

Despite the hardships of the trail, settlers continued to pour into the Oregon country. By 1845, more than three thousand immigrants to the Pacific Northwest had already come over the Oregon Trail. The goal of many of the pioneers was the rich Willamette Valley. Here, and in other favored regions, the new settlers once again began a frontier existence, bringing with them the cooking experiences of the region from which they had come and adapting these to the new food resources—the fruits, the berries, the nuts, and the wealth of fish and seafood of the Pacific Northwest.

Fish and seafood cookery is an outstanding feature of the cuisines of Washington and Oregon. Salmon, the great staple of the Indians, is still widely eaten, but is prepared today in a great many more ways than the Chinooks ever imagined. Northwesterners bake, stuff, fry, broil, boil, smoke, pickle, can, and barbecue their salmon.

Barbecued salmon is fresh salmon baked with vegetables (onions, garlic, green peppers, tomatoes), herbs, and spices. The vegetables cook to a tangy barbecuelike sauce which is served spooned atop the tender steaming pink fish. The list of salmon specialties continues at length: Puget Sound salmon roll (flaked cooked salmon rolled in biscuit dough, baked, and served with a tomato sauce); jellied salmon (a cold buffet dish of poached salmon molded in gelatin, beautifully garnished); salmon soufflé (salmon in a rich creamy mixture baked to golden fluffiness and served with melted butter). Northwesterners slice leftover salmon soufflé and fry it for breakfast, much as Charlestonians enjoy shrimp paste with their morning grits and New Englanders delight in codfish balls for Sunday breakfast.

Pacific Coast halibut and sturgeon are also prized fishes, while the seafood of this area ranges from the tiny fingernail-sized Olympia oyster to a giant ten-pound clam known as the *geoduck* (pronounced goo-ey-duck). Geoduck hunting is a highly challenging sport on the beaches of Puget Sound at low tide. One geoduck hunter hangs on to the slippery two-foot neck of the clam while the other frantically digs a hole in the sand to unearth the body which is partially encased in a shell.

The geoduck immediately begins to burrow its way deeper underground when attacked, so success at catching a geoduck is really something to celebrate. So is the dinner that follows, for the muscle clinging to the clam's shell is exceedingly tender, and is delicious sliced and broiled. The neck is chopped and used in chowder. Because of its scarcity, however, one is not likely to get a taste of geoduck outside of the Puget Sound area.

The name *geoduck* is reputedly derived from the fact that

THE COOKERY OF THE PACIFIC NORTHWEST

the shape of this huge clam resembles that of a duck. But it should also be noted that the word is sometimes spelled *goeduck* and sometimes *gweduc,* and is actually of Chinook Indian origin.

Other varieties of clams are more plentiful on the Washington and Oregon beaches, particularly the varieties known as butter clams, money-shell clams, and the larger razor clams, so named because their shape resembles that of an old-fashioned straight razor. Olympia oysters, too, are enjoyed in abundance, either sucked raw from the shell and eaten with cocktail sauce, or cooked until plump in a hot spicy sauce and served on toast, a dish that goes by the name of oyster pan roast.

Fresh-water crawfish from the tributaries of the Columbia River in Oregon are boiled in spiced and seasoned water and served in the shell, looking like tiny lobsters, about a dozen of them to a serving. In contrast to these miniature shellfish are the jumbo Dungeness crabs of the Pacific coast. Surely the most famous of West Coast crabmeat dishes is crab Louis, originally created in Seattle by a San Francisco chef. Crab Louis is a cold dish of lumps of tender crabmeat lavished in a sauce of mayonnaise, chili sauce, and whipped cream. It is usually garnished with wedges of tomato and hard-cooked egg.

As distinguished as its seafood cookery is the fruit cookery of the Pacific Northwest. As early as 1847, eight hundred fruit trees brought overland from Iowa were planted in western Oregon. These trees yielded fruits that were the forerunners of today's renowned Rogue River pears, Willamette Valley plums and prunes, Hood River apples, and Dalles cherries. Wild berries, native to the Pacific Northwest, had greeted the first white settlers years earlier. Especially abundant were the blackberries that grew in many varieties and were used by the newly arrived Oregon Trail folk in a dessert they called summer pudding.

This luscious concoction was prepared by arranging layers of buttered white bread and stewed sweetened blackberries in a deep pudding dish. A plate or other weight was set firmly atop the pudding to press the juice into the bread slices until they were sweet and cakelike, sodden with the rich purple stain. Then the pudding was set aside to chill, if possible, and was served cold with heavy cream.

Other berries, including many cultivated varieties, are plentiful and popular in Washington and Oregon today—the dewberry (a low-growing blackberry), the loganberry (a cross between the red raspberry and the blackberry, developed in 1881 by Judge J. H. Logan of California), the youngberry (a large sweet wine-colored version of the dewberry, named for its developer, B. M. Young), the raspberry, strawberry and cranberry.

But fruit cookery is not limited to desserts, traditional or otherwise, in the Pacific Northwest. Cherry omelets and cold cherry soups; purple plum chutney (a spicy fruit relish); Oregon grape jelly; and Western pot roast (beef stewed with onions, cider, brown sugar, and dried apricots and prunes) are all specialties of this region.

Nuts, too, are in excellent supply, particularly filberts and walnuts. From Oregon filbert groves, Northwesterners pre-

pare filbert waffles (with chopped filberts and drained crushed pineapple), bake fragrant nutted cookies known as filbert crescents, and often sprinkle chopped filberts atop the crusts of their apple pies before baking.

Game cookery dates back to early hunting and trapping days in the Northwest. Pigeon pie, an old pioneer recipe, was prepared with the dark-meated band-tailed pigeon that frequented the Rocky Mountain and Pacific coast areas. The pigeons, six or so, were dressed and cleaned, browned in salt-pork fat, and then simmered with carrots, onions, and other vegetables until tender. A thickened sauce was made of the stew liquid, and the pigeons and gravy were then baked in a casserole with a pastry top—really a wild-bird version of chicken pie.

Pigeon pie also went by the name of dove pie or potted doves. Grouse, too, filled many a dinner pot. Broiled elk steaks, venison cutlets, and venison cakes (prepared with ground venison and cooked like hamburger) were, and still are, popular in the Pacific Northwest.

While enterprising settlers continued to stream into the Oregon country during the 1840s, California just to the south of it remained a sleepy and undeveloped stretch of coastline, governed by Mexico. Despite scattered descriptions of California's eternally springlike climate, the oranges and other remarkable fruits grown in the mission gardens, and of the wild Spanish horses and cattle that roamed the countryside, few Americans showed interest in this far-off place.

CALIFORNIA GOLD RUSH DAYS AND THE HANGTOWN FRY

When John Bidwell, leader of the first overland party to cross the Sierra Nevadas, arrived in California in 1841, he estimated the number of Americans there to be fewer than one hundred. Nor were these a very attractive lot, for they consisted chiefly of bearded and unkempt mountain men from the Rockies, horse thieves who had come to drive off animals by the hundreds, and runaway sailors who had jumped ship in various ports along the Pacific coast.

The missions founded by the Spanish Franciscan priests, and the cattle and sheep ranches of the Mexican *patróns* were the chief centers of civilization, and even these were shockingly crude. The first of the Spanish missions had been built in 1769 at San Diego under the leadership of Father Junipero Serra. Until 1823, the Franciscan friars continued to build missions along El Camino Real or "the royal road," at a distance considered then to be "a day's journey apart." The final mission in the chain of twenty-one was built at Sonoma, north of San Francisco.

The Indians of California submitted to life on the mission farms where, under the guidance of the padres, they tilled the soil, harvested crops, sheared sheep, worked cattle hides for leather, and became converts to Christianity. Wheat, corn, beans, and squash were grown on the mission farms, and most missions also cultivated olive groves and vineyards. Pears, apricots, pomegranates, figs, oranges, and lemons were produced. All of these fruits, as well as the olives and the wheat that were grown, had originally been introduced by the Spanish.

On the ranches, however, cattle and sheep were the prime concern, and little if any fruit was to be had, with the exception of the prickly pear. The towns were almost as rural and as unequipped with the conveniences of the day as were the ranches and the missions. Transportation, even for the families of wealthy landowners, was either on horseback or by wooden-wheeled cart drawn by oxen, and according to John Bidwell, "there was not a hotel in San Francisco or Monterey or anywhere in California until 1846." In that year the Americans declared California independent of Mexico, and two years later, at the close of the Mexican War, she was formally ceded to the United States.

The year 1848 also saw the discovery of gold in California at Sutter's Fort, not far from the present city of Sacramento. John Sutter, a Swiss, had come to the California coast by ship in 1839. He bought out the holdings of Russian fur traders at Fort Ross, north of San Francisco, and then traveled inland to establish a colony which he called New Helvetia. In an effort to pay his business debts, Sutter undertook a number of enterprises including wheat growing, ranching, river freighting to and from San Francisco, and lumbering. It was while building a sawmill on Sutter's property that an employee, James Marshall, discovered in the clear shallow water of the millrace a nugget of gold.

Despite the slow communications of the day, California was soon inundated with gold seekers. The year 1849 saw the largest influx in her brief history, and by 1850 the population of California had swelled to the point where she was admitted to the Union.

Unlike the preceding waves of pioneers, who had advanced across the country building new homes and leaving permanent settlements behind them when they moved on, the gold seekers were not family folk. Few women and almost no children made the trip to California. Indeed, women were estimated to number only about 8 per cent of the population during gold rush days. The immigrants were men, few of whom planned to settle the country. Most were interested in obtaining what wealth they could and then returning to their families in the Midwest, the East, or the South. In this respect the California forty-niners may be likened to the Jamestown adventurers and fortune seekers of 1607. The fate of many of them was easily as disastrous.

The route to California from the East was still precarious in 1849. Some of the prospectors used overland trails like the Oregon and the Santa Fe, while others went by ship around Cape Horn at the tip of South America. Still others, seeking a shorter route from the East coast, took ship from New York to Central America, then made their way on foot or by mule across the steaming Panama jungles, continuing their journey by boat from Panama City to San Francisco.

This shortest route took about thirty-four days, but many died of fevers during the voyage, and swindles and deceptions were practiced at every turn on the gold-hungry travelers. Tales were told in the California mining camps of one New York shipping company that took advance fares for the journey, only to leave its victims stranded at Panama City waiting for a California-bound vessel that never came.

Once in California, the miners found living conditions to

be the crudest imaginable and food and drink unbelievably expensive. It was true that supplies of food, tools, and wearing apparel had been brought to California at great cost by the storekeepers who sold them, but profits were also enormous. Whisky that cost five cents a drink in St. Louis was fifty cents in San Francisco, poured from a pitcher on the bar and served in a tin cup. Nevertheless, many miners drank to excess, with gambling, shootings, and general carousing the order of the day in the gold-town saloons.

While the cost of whisky might be ignored, the cost of food could not. Bread and onions sold for one dollar a pound. A tiny loaf, which one writer of the time described as "only a fair-sized biscuit," sold for fifty cents, and professional hunters coming into town with venison or bear hacked the meat into chunks which they sold for a little less than their weight in gold. Eggs were fifty cents each, and "butter" was manufactured by ingenious methods using ingredients like beef, sheep, or bear tallow, and lard. This inferior grade of oleomargarine was passed off as butter and sold at high prices to miners who frankly admitted that it had been so long since they'd tasted the real thing, they couldn't tell the difference. Chicken was a complete rarity, but the half-wild Spanish cattle that had formerly been slaughtered chiefly for their hides and tallow now supplied beef, coarse and stringy though it was, to the miners. Most purchases were paid off in gold dust, weighed out in ounces.

Life in the hills where the mining camps were located was, if anything, even worse than that in the towns. The much-praised California climate lay to the south and the west of the mining country. Deep snows, bitter cold, driving winds, and disastrous rainstorms were the lot of most prospectors who spent any length of time testing or working claims in the foothills of the Sierras. In summer the weather was usually extremely dry, with cold nights and with days of intense heat, the temperature soaring to well over 100 degrees at midday.

Bacon, flour, and coffee were foods the miners carried with them into the hills. In winter, snow was kneaded with the flour, and from this stiff dough, bread was baked at an open fire. The fat from frying bacon was often dripped onto the bread to make it more tasty. When provisions ran out, the miners chewed on the inner bark of the sugar pine or went hungry until they reached a camp or other place of supply. One miner wrote of arriving desperately hungry at a rude unfinished hotel being built in a valley in the mining country. Here a throng of two hundred men milled about waiting for a meal. After some time the miner obtained a place at a long, crowded puncheon table and received a lunch of fried bacon, bread, and coffee for which he cheerfully measured out three dollars in gold dust.

It is not surprising, therefore, that the Hangtown fry should have been considered a meal fit for a king during California gold rush days—and worth nearly a king's ransom in gold dust. Hangtown was a base of supply for a large section of the mining region. Its site was originally known as Old Dry Diggins, but was shortly labeled Hangtown, for it was said that five men had been hanged there on the same day and from the same tree. So great was Hangtown's reputation for violence and lawlessness during the gold rush that she later changed her name to Placerville and became a settled and respectable community. Other gold rush towns also bore colorful names such as Red-Dog, You-Bet, and Ground Hog Glory.

Legend has it that a miner who had struck it rich on his claim came swaggering into Hangtown one day demanding the best meal he could get. Cost was no object. He was subsequently served a mountainous meal of fried oysters, fried eggs, and bacon. Ordering a Hangtown fry thereafter became a mark of prosperity for gold-rich miners, the status symbol of its day.

The California gold rush was followed during the next half century by the discovery of gold in Oregon, Montana, and Idaho, and of both gold and silver in Nevada and Colorado. The mines attracted many European immigrant groups, including Yugoslavs, Scandinavians, Irishmen, Manxmen (from the Isle of Man), and Cornishmen. Touches of these and other foreign cuisines are still in evidence today in some sections of the West.

THE COOKERY OF CALIFORNIA

The roar and the tumult of the California gold rush was destined to subside—and eventually, of course, it did. Placer mining (panning the streams for gold) dwindled as pickings became poorer. Prospectors who could not afford to set up the more costly operation of shaft mining were forced to go to work for others. As more and more of the rich claims were taken, many miners gave up completely. Some went on to the silver mines of Nevada and Colorado where the work was hot, deep, and dangerous, but paid fairly well. Others stayed on in California, sent for their families, and became tradesmen and farmers. Soon grain fields and orchards began to appear in the Great Valley that lay between the Sierra Nevadas and the Coast Range. By the 1880s, land-hungry settlers had replaced the gold-hungry miners of an earlier day.

One of the dishes of the California land settlers was red-flannel stew. This colorful, spicy concoction was a variation on New England's red-flannel hash, brought west by stages over a period of nearly two hundred years. Red-flannel stew was made with chopped cooked corned beef, but instead of being hashed along with leftover potatoes and beets, the corned beef was combined with such Western ingredients as beans and chili peppers. Tomatoes, onion, and garlic also went into this tasty dish.

In the early 1860s an entirely new and exotic food influence entered the West by way of the port of San Francisco. Thousands of Chinese were brought to California to work on the transcontinental railroad then being built eastward across the Sierras. Many Chinese became cooks in the lumber, mining, and railroad camps of the West, and later opened restaurants of their own. San Francisco's Chinatown became a source of special Chinese foods—bean sprouts, bamboo shoots, water chestnuts, snow peas and, for the very sophisticated taste, cuttlefish and shark fins.

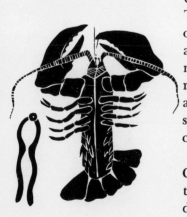

From the Chinese community here, and in other West Coast cities, came not only the chow meins and chop sueys, the won tons, foo yongs, and superb lobster and shrimp dishes, but new and improved cookery styles. Especially valu-

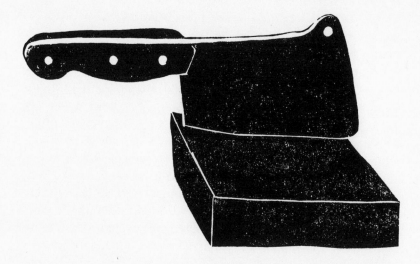

able is the Chinese method of cooking vegetables quickly
(by a sautéing-plus-steaming process), and serving them still
crisp and deliciously fresh-tasting. The age-old necessity in
their own country for using as little cooking fuel as possible
made the Chinese experts at quick cooking. This also ex-
plains why most Chinese dishes consist of foods that have
been finely cut or thinly sliced *before* cooking.

The completion of the transcontinental railroad in 1869
opened the West to immigrants from Europe as well as from
the eastern two-thirds of the United States. Italian, Portuguese, and Greek fishermen were among the many national
groups that flocked to the California coast.

A special contribution of the Italian fishermen of San
Francisco (although the Portuguese claim this one, too) is
the famous fish stew known as *cioppino* (pronounced cho-
peen-o). *Cioppino* may be prepared with as many as a dozen
kinds of fish and shellfish—striped bass, halibut, rock cod,
shrimps, lobsters, oysters, and crabs—or as few as two kinds
of fish. It all depends on what the day's catch is like. The
fish is cut into pieces and cooked with a sauce of garlic,
tomatoes, green peppers, parsley, celery, and onions. The
crabs, lobsters, clams, or other shellfish may be left in the
shell or removed. Red or white wine or sherry is usually
included in the stew, and it is traditional to serve *cioppino*

(which is closely related to the French bouillabaisse of New Orleans) in deep soup bowls. Wine and hot, crusty sourdough bread are popular accompaniments for *cioppino*.

The origin of the word *cioppino* is something of a mystery. Many believe that it is Italian-American for "chip in," as this dish is said to be the result of each fisherman's adding something from his day's catch to the communal stew kettle on the wharf. Today many waterside San Francisco restaurants feature *cioppino*.

Other fish dishes that are found almost exclusively in California are prepared with red or pink abalone, an unusual native shellfish. The abalone consists mainly of a large muscular foot partially encased in an ear-shaped shell. The lining of the shell supplies mother-of-pearl for buttons and other ornaments.

When abalone is prepared for cooking, the meat is first pounded with a wooden mallet to tenderize it. Abalone steaks may then be broiled, baked, or fried, or the meat may be chopped and combined with diced fried bacon, onion, potatoes, and milk or cream for an abalone chowder. This dish is much like the New England clam chowder of the East coast.

Large and luscious Dungeness crabs as well as tender little three-inch-long sand dabs rank high in California fish popularity. Sand dabs are usually rolled in flour and fried in butter, then served with lemon juice, melted butter, and parsley. Dungeness crab, named for a village on the Juan de Fuca Strait in northwestern Washington, is generally caught along the Pacific coast from Alaska to San Francisco, and almost nowhere else. It is served in a great variety of ways in California, ranging from barbecued crab (crabmeat simmered in a zesty sauce) to baked avocados stuffed with crabmeat.

Avocados, sometimes called alligator pears, are a great favorite in California cookery. Chilled, cut into cubes, and served as an avocado cocktail with a sharp dressing, this bland fruit with its subtle flavor makes a fine first-course appetizer. Californians also often mash the buttery yellow-green flesh of the avocado, season it for piquancy, and serve it as an appetizer dip or spread, the *guacamole* of Mexico and the Southwest. But these are only beginnings. There are avocado soups, main-course baked avocados, avocado salads, and even an avocado frozen pudding and an avocado ice cream!

Like the avocado, which was native to Mexico and Central America, the Spanish also brought the *chayote* to southern California in mission days. This subtropical squash, sometimes called the mango squash and sometimes the vegetable pear, has a flavor much like that of summer squash, but more delicate. California cooks like to halve chayotes, fill their scooped-out centers with a seasoned mixture of chopped beef, rice, tomatoes, and sautéed chayote pulp, and then bake them to make a delectable supper dish known as stuffed chayote.

California grows almost every variety of vegetable in the world. She has popularized broccoli, zucchini, and the thistle-like globe artichoke largely through the efforts of the many Italian immigrants who turned to vegetable growing in the rich soil of her valleys.

Grape culture, too, was undertaken in California by Italian and other European immigrants. Today California's vineyards supply a flourishing wine industry which has, in turn, been highly influential in bringing native wines to the

American dinner table and popularizing the use of wine in American cookery.

California's fruits, like her vegetables, are of bounteous output. Californians are as likely to start their day with fresh figs in cream, ripe papaya sprinkled with lime juice, or chilled pomegranate juice as with the more conventional, but equally native, orange juice or grapefruit half.

Apricots, prunes, raisins, dates, and English walnuts, all of which grow so prolifically in California, are the ingredients of cakes, breads, muffins, cookies, pies, puddings, and luscious desserts like smooth, rich apricot mousse and airy prune whip.

The California prune industry began in the mid-nineteenth century when a Frenchman named Pellier grafted a variety of French prune plum to the root stock of the native wild plum in the Santa Clara Valley. The result was a plum that would dry perfectly without fermentation around the pit, a most important requirement for any prune plum. In the American West, plums suitable for drying are usually called prunes even while they are still on the tree.

Tropical, citrus, and other fruits are often eaten fresh at the close of a meal in California, but tangy orange shortcake, fluffy lemon chiffon pie, or a glamorous date torte crowned with whipped cream are regional desserts that can seldom be resisted.

FOOD PRODUCTS OF THE WEST TODAY

Montana and Wyoming are primarily engaged in the raising of beef cattle and sheep, particularly in the Great Plains region in the eastern portions of these states. Wheat, potatoes, dry beans, and sugar beets are important field crops, and both states have sugar-beet refineries. In addition, Montana grows cherries as well as apples and several varieties of berries in the valleys west of the Continental Divide.

Colorado, too, is an important livestock-raising state, with beef cattle grazing on her eastern plains, and sheep to be found in the more rugged country. Sugar beets, which were

introduced by German immigrants in 1899, are a leading crop in Colorado, and her irrigated river valleys produce fine cauliflower, onions, lettuce, and other vegetables, as well as apples, peaches, and cantaloupes.

Dairying and poultrying, including turkey raising, are prominent, and Colorado honey is considered sweeter and richer than most because her high dry climate quickly evaporates its moisture.

In addition to her famed potatoes, Idaho grows wheat, peas, and sugar beets. Utah, too, produces large yields of potatoes, as well as wheat, small grains, and sugar beets. Both states are active in sheep and cattle raising. Vegetable and fruit growing may be largely attributed to the industry of the Mormon farmers who settled in Utah in 1847 and subsequently irrigated much of that state and of her neighboring states, proving that arid lands could be made to bloom.

Irrigated valleys of Idaho produce apples, plums, pears, and cherries. In Utah, apricots and peaches are grown in addition, with figs, pomegranates, and some citrus fruits produced in the extreme southern portion. A most important industry is the processing of potatoes into dehydrated potato flakes (for instant mashed potatoes) and frozen French fries.

Cattle and sheep raising are predominant in Nevada, but in the semitropical southeastern portion of the state almonds, figs, grapes, and pomegranates are grown.

Washington and Oregon are rich in the fruits of the sea as well as those of the land. Apples, pears, plums and prunes, cherries, peaches, cranberries, raspberries, and blackberries are produced in both states. Loganberries and youngberries, hybrids of the latter two berry fruits, are also grown, as are excellent crops of filberts and walnuts.

From the rivers and sea come salmon, halibut, tuna, crabs, clams, oysters, and crawfish. Salmon and tuna canning are important industries in the Pacific Northwest. Dairying, poultrying, and the production of honey are also prominent in Washington and Oregon. In the eastern portions of these states, wheat is grown and cattle ranching is extensive. Canning and freezing of the abundant harvests of fruits and vegetables are vital industries.

It should be noted that the state of Washington leads the nation in apple production, and that her five types of salmon —chinook, red, silver, pink, and chum—make her the principal fish-cannery center of the world.

California has come a long way from the days of acorn harvesting. Her range of fruits includes temperate zone, semi-

tropical, and tropical varieties—apples, peaches, pears, cherries, nectarines, plums, prunes, apricots, oranges, grapefruits, lemons, melons, berries of many kinds, and the more exotic avocado, papaya, Oriental persimmon, prickly pear, pomegranate, mango, and guava, as well as figs and dates.

California grapes are grown in table, raisin, and wine varieties. Her wineries supply a major percentage of domestic wines. Olives are in abundant supply, and California is a major source of almonds and walnuts.

Vegetables grown in California are so numerous that even a partial list is a very long one: lettuce, asparagus, peas, Brussels sprouts, spinach, beans, tomatoes, artichokes, broccoli, zucchini, celery, cauliflower, and many, many more of great commercial importance.

Finally, California fisheries yield tuna, sardines, flounder, mackerel, sand dabs, abalone, crabs, and other varieties. The packing of fish and shellfish, particularly through freezing and canning, is a thriving industry.

BAKED STUFFED IDAHO POTATOES

RECIPES OF THE WEST TO TRY

(4 servings)

4	medium-large or 5 medium Idaho baking potatoes
4 to 6	tablespoons butter or margarine
1/2	teaspoon salt
1/4	teaspoon seasoned salt
1/8	teaspoon white pepper
2	tablespoons milk or cream

Scrub potatoes well, dry and pierce all over with a long-tined fork. Rub the skins lightly with a little oil or other shortening. Bake potatoes at 400 degrees for 3/4 to 1 hour, or until soft; or bake in potato baker on range top until done. Place potatoes on flattest side and cut about a 1/2-inch slice from across the top, leaving a deep boat-shaped bottom portion. Carefully scoop out potato and place in a mixing bowl, leaving the shells intact. (Scoop potato from top slice also, and discard skin.)

Add remaining ingredients to hot potato and mash well until blended and very smooth. Taste for seasoning. Pile potato mixture back into shells, leaving rounded tops. Dot with additional butter and dust with paprika. All this may be done several hours in advance of serving. To serve potatoes, heat in a 375-degree oven for 10 to 15 minutes, or until heated through and golden brown and slightly crusty on top.

If *very* large potatoes are used, bake as directed, then cut into horizontal halves and fill both with potato mixture. Larger potatoes will take longer to bake. One potato should provide two servings, in this case.

CALIFORNIA DATE AND WALNUT BREAD

(one 9 x 5 loaf)

1	cup pitted dates, cut into 1/4-inch pieces
1	cup sugar
1	cup boiling water
1/2	cup vegetable shortening
2	eggs, well beaten
2	cups sifted all-purpose flour
1 1/2	teaspoons baking soda
1/2	teaspoon salt
1	cup walnuts, coarsely chopped
1	teaspoon vanilla

Place dates and sugar in a large mixing bowl. Add shortening to boiling water and keep water simmering until shortening is melted. Pour this mixture immediately over dates and sugar, and stir until sugar is dissolved. Cool slightly.

Add eggs, beating mixture well as you do so. Combine flour, soda, and salt. Sift into date mixture, stirring until well blended. Batter may be slightly lumpy. Add walnuts and vanilla.

Turn batter into a 9 x 5-inch loaf pan which has been well greased. Bake at 325 degrees for 1 hour, or until center of loaf springs back to touch. Cool thoroughly on wire rack. To release loaf from pan, run a thin sharp knife around the edges, invert onto rack, and tap lightly.

To serve Date and Walnut Bread cut into thin slices with a sharp knife. It is delicious with cream cheese or with butter and marmalade or jelly. It may be made up into small fancy-shaped sandwiches and served with a fruit salad. Date and Walnut Bread keeps well for days in a tin, or wrapped in heavy foil.

alaska

STRAWBERRIES the size of your fist; sunflowers 12 feet tall; 90-degree temperatures in July, and far too many mosquitoes. Does this sound like Alaska, the icebound land?

Here is another picture. Seal blubber and caribou flesh eaten raw; soil so hardened with permafrost that no seed can ever be planted in it; fog-ridden offshore islands where sunshine has never been recorded.

Which of these is Alaska? Both, of course, for this is the Great Land, in the translation of the Aleut-derived word *Al-ay-ek-sa*—a Great Land that is more than *twice* the size of Texas, that extends into the Arctic Ocean to within 1,200 miles of the North Pole, and into the Pacific to within shouting distance of the Soviet Union!

The forty-ninth state is a land of varied regions and of many startling contrasts. Consider her southeastern Panhandle, a narrow ledge of land that lies between steep coastal mountains and the sea. Here the harbors of the cities never freeze, due to the warm Japan Current. Forests cover the mountainsides, and flowers grow in profusion. Rainfall is abundant, there is little snow except in the higher elevations, winters are mild and summers cool. The city of Sitka, located on an island in the Panhandle region, averages the same annual temperature as Washington, D.C. Juneau, the capital, and Ketchikan, a large fish-canning center, are also here in the Panhandle. In all three cities, the winters are considerably kinder than they are in many cities of the Midwest and Great Plains, a thousand miles to the south.

Now let us turn to the Arctic slope, the top third of Alaska that lies within the Arctic Circle. Here is the bleak northern coastal plain, vast stretches of treeless tundra carpeted with mosses, lichens, and hundreds of varieties of wildflowers during the short Arctic summer, crusted with deep snow throughout most of the year. The Arctic Ocean, open for only about two months in summer, is even then clogged with floating ice, and the average annual temperature in this Arctic region is about 8 degrees above zero.

In Barrow, located on a tip of land that juts into the Arctic Ocean (and now the northernmost town in the United States), the sun goes down on about November 15 and does not reappear for two months. Darkness and the deep freeze settle in on the fifteen hundred Eskimo inhabitants and the one hundred or so non-native residents of this outpost at the top of the world.

The Alaskan interior, known as the central plateau or the Yukon River Basin, presents a slightly less formidable aspect. Winter ends here in April, followed by a May thaw. In June the days are eighteen to twenty hours long. The temperature often soars into the sweltering nineties at this time, for the "nights" consist of but a few hours of twilight, and there is no cooling-off period before the sun once again appears. Thus intense heat is built up. In areas like the Tanana Valley near the interior city of Fairbanks, there is good farming during the brief summer. Cereal grains, potatoes, turnips, carrots, beets, peas, cabbage, cauliflower, lettuce, spinach, and even tomatoes all grow here with the

lightning speed of animated-cartoon vegetables.

Winter, however, presents a stark picture in the Alaskan interior where the inland location and northerly latitude make for extremes like the minus 81 degrees recorded just across the Alaska line in Canada in 1947. Nor are readings of 50 to 60 degrees below zero uncommon here between October and April.

Permafrost, a condition of eternally frozen subsoil, afflicts the northern two thirds of Alaska making deep-rooted plant life impossible. In areas where the topsoil thaws to a depth of two feet or so in summer, planting may of course be undertaken. But there are many sections of the interior and on the Arctic slope where only the top six inches of the soil ever thaw.

Wherever permafrost is present, great surface puddles, some as large as lakes, form during May and June, for the melting snow cannot drain downward to the hard frost layer beneath. Such excellent breeding conditions bring forth swarms of gnats, flies, and mosquitoes each summer to molest cattle and other livestock and to plague man with a fury that is seldom equaled even in the tropics.

South central Alaska, sheltered from Arctic winds by the Alaska Range to the north and warmed by the Japan Current to the south, is again a somewhat gentler region. Alaska's largest city, Anchorage, is here, and amid the distant backdrop of the Alaska Range towers Mount McKinley, some 20,300 feet high, monarch of all North American peaks.

Some fifty miles from Anchorage lies the fertile Matanuska Valley which grows nearly two thirds of Alaska's farm products and provides fresh milk, poultry, and eggs to a population that once knew only canned milk and rarely tasted domestic fowl. Farming began in this valley as an agricultural experiment in 1935. During that peak depression year, the United States Government transported some two hundred farm families from the relief rolls of Minnesota, Wisconsin, and Michigan to Alaska to begin a new life. Each pioneering family received a tract of land, basic farm buildings, and livestock, but even with these aids the process of adjustment was difficult. A long, frigid winter in a strange new land, where children had to go off to school in darkness and return in darkness, was hard going. Old homes, friends, and family in the far-off states were severely missed.

However, the long and pleasant hours of daylight in summer, the fast-growing crops, and the financial returns of the harvest were strong compensating factors. Today in the Matanuska Valley the brief intense growing season produces lush fields of wheat and other grains, and root and leafy vegetables, including especially fine potatoes. One example of the effect of continuous growing hours on field vegetables is seen in the enormous cabbages of the Matanuska region,

weighing not five pounds, not ten pounds, but up to *sixty*
pounds each! Some turn up yearly at fairs and expositions,
with the 40- and 50-pounders crowding the ranks as runners-
up.

The Aleutians of southwestern Alaska are really a mountain range that curves more than a thousand miles westward
into the Pacific. This range, which attaches to the mainland
in the form of the Alaska Peninsula, gradually strings out
in a series of partly sunken volcanic islands, treeless, foggy,
and almost always in the grip of rain or snow. The Aleutian
Islands have been among the least agriculturally productive
areas of Alaska, although the native Aleuts who inhabit them
are now beginning to raise sheep and other livestock. These
islands, which have the appearance of stepping stones between Asia and America, may at one time have served as an
effective bridge between the two continents for peoples migrating from the East to the West.

North of the Aleutians in the fog-shrouded Bering Sea
lie the Pribilof Islands, summer home of the fur seals, and

the large islands of Nunivak and St. Lawrence, now set aside as bird and game reserves. Still farther north, situated in the 56-mile wide Bering Strait between the Soviet Union and Alaska, are the small islands known as the Diomedes. Big Diomede Island belongs to the Soviet Union and Little Diomede to the United States. Although only two and one-half miles apart, the International Date Line runs between the two islands—and when it is Sunday on Little Diomede, it is Monday on Big Diomede.

The native Alaskans—Indians, Eskimos, and Aleuts—have shown a remarkable adaptability to their land. For the Eskimos and the Aleuts especially, survival has always hung by a thread, and before the diseases of the white man were introduced mass deaths were always due to starvation rather than any other cause.

THE FOODS OF THE NATIVE ALASKANS

The Indians of the Panhandle and the southern coast lived in the most amiable environment of Alaska. Like the Indians of the Pacific Northwest, these people were salmon fishermen. They were also wood carvers whose artistry produced the curious and impressive totem poles that stood as a coat of arms before each dwelling, and served to tell the legends and the history of the families within.

With wood so plentiful along the moist, rainy Pacific coast, the Tlingit and other Alaskan tribes built their large, gabled houses of wood, carved great cedar dugout canoes capable of carrying fifty or more, and even cooked their food in wooden boxes, via the stone-boiling method.

No agriculture was practiced by the Alaskan Indians, for there were wild edible roots and berries aplenty in the forests and along the shore. There was abundant game, too, in the forests, but venison and other meat was often bypassed for fish: salmon, herring, cod, halibut, trout, clams, shrimp, and crabs. But the Indians of the Alaskan coast did not limit their food gathering to the river bank, the seashore, and the offshore waters. These were an ocean-going people who

made long voyages hundreds of miles out to sea in their
outsized canoes, from which they hunted seals, porpoises,
sea otter, and even whales. Fish were, of course, preserved
for year-round eating by drying, just as buffalo meat was
preserved by the Plains Indians in the form of jerky or
pemmican.

Unlike most North American tribes, the Tlingits and their
neighbors had a highly organized society that included aristocrats, commoners, and slaves. An important feature of the
life of the aristocracy was the potlatch, a great feast with
singing and dancing at which the wealthy head of a household would distribute sumptuous gifts to the assembled
guests. Magnificent blankets, fine basketry and wood carvings,
jewelry, and even canoes were among the presentations. The
recipients of such gifts were obliged to repay them with even
more grandeur at a later date, and those who did not, or
who failed to meet the expected standard, fell into everlasting disgrace. So great was the emphasis on social prestige,
as measured by material possessions, that a wealthy slave-
owner might occasionally club a few of his slaves to death
in public (with a handsome implement especially designed
for the purpose) just to show how free he could afford to be
with his property.

No such luxury was permitted the Eskimo, who inhabited
the western and northern regions of Alaska, obtaining much
of his food from the chilly waters of the Bering Sea and the
Arctic Ocean. Although the Eskimo's custom of putting his
old people out on the ice to perish in time of severe food
shortage seems cruel and barbaric, he at least had a sound
social reason. The old and the useless had to make way for
the vigorous and the young, the present and future sustainers
of life. In the Arctic there was only so much food to go
around.

Although the coming of the white man has introduced
many new foods into the Eskimo diet, even in remote parts
of Alaska, many Eskimos still hunt the foods of their ancestors. Game animals include the caribou (a wild member
of the reindeer family), moose, Dall sheep (a relative of
the bighorn sheep), mountain goat, polar bear, Arctic hare

(brown in summer and white in winter), and geese, eider ducks, and other wild fowl.

The bulky, long-haired musk ox, once a favorite Eskimo food animal, became extinct in Alaska in the 1870s due to overhunting. Musk oxen from Greenland have since been imported to Nunivak Island. Prized for their beeflike flesh (which carries no trace of musk odor) and their rich creamy milk, the growing herd on Nunivak is now protected from the ravages of bears (to which they were subject on the mainland) and unauthorized slaughter by man.

Similarly, the caribou, once the mainstay of the Eskimo diet, became seriously depleted in the late 1800s. In the winter of 1878–79, three entire Eskimo villages on St. Lawrence Island starved to death. Later, the reindeer, the smaller semidomestic cousin of the caribou, was imported from Siberia.

On the Alaskan mainland game such as caribou is seen in the Arctic region only during the brief summer when the animals come north to feed on the mosses and lichens of the blooming tundra. In the early spring the Eskimo, also hungry for growing things, eats first of all the undigested greens that he finds in the stomach of the newly slain caribou. Wild cranberries and blueberries, the edible low-growing plants of the tundra, and eggs taken from the nests of wild birds all add variety to the Eskimo menu in summer.

Later in the summer, as cold weather approaches, game that is not eaten at once can be frozen. This method of preservation is of course much simpler than the drying process used by the Indians, and renders food tastier and more nutritious. It has also been the direct inspiration for the food-freezing methods that are used throughout the world today.

Many Eskimo tribes are nomadic or seminomadic in their never-ending search for food. However, the sea, frozen or liquid, is a recurrent source of supply. In the single-manned kayak or in the larger family-sized umiak (skin boats, both), the Eskimo goes forth on the open waters in search of seal, walrus, and whale. A special treat, obtained through secondary means, is the cache of undigested clams found in the walrus' stomach. So fond of this nourishing seafood is the Eskimo that he invariably slits open the stomach of his kill first. The walrus, who also loves clams, has obligingly dug these from the sandy bottom of shallow sea waters.

In winter, when the seas and rivers are closed, the Eskimo hunts seal, walrus, and fish through openings in the ice. Today, when airplanes fly canned fruit salad and corn on the cob to Eskimo-populated towns like Barrow on the Arctic Ocean, the government-employed Eskimo still prefers to take his vacation in spring so that he can go whale hunting as did his ancestors.

Most Eskimo foods were eaten raw in the past, for the lack of wood or other fuel made cooking unlikely, and frozen meats or fish chewed on awhile became quite tasty and tender. Some cooking was done, however, over a fire of precious seal oil, which was also used to provide light and enough heat for drying clothes. *Muktuk,* whale skin with a thick layer of blubber (fat) attached, was a nourishing and warming food eaten raw. A delicacy resembling ice cream was *akutok,* a well-beaten concoction of seal oil, berries, and caribou or reindeer fat.

Today the Eskimo diet is a bizarre mixture of foods both old and new. The icy climate still makes demands on the body which are best met with fats and nourishing raw meats. Yet the colorful canned and packaged foods of the world outside exert a powerful tug at Eskimo appetites. Eskimo children chew on raw walrus kidney and chocolate-covered candy bars with equal gusto; the Eskimo whale hunter, resting on a chunk of floating ice in the Arctic Ocean, sips coffee from Brazil as he awaits his prey.

The introduction of complex, refined foods, high in sugar and starch content, has of course taken its toll in terms of toothaches and cavities. Eskimo teeth, once so strong that they could wrench nails from driftwood boards, are today often in a state of such decay that the northland has become a dentist's paradise, and it is not uncommon to meet young Eskimo men and women wearing dentures.

Unlike the Alaskan Indians, the Eskimos had no slaves or aristocrats in their society. All were considered equal and all shared food equally in time of plenty. The beach of an Eskimo village located on the Bering Sea or the Arctic Ocean was its main street. Here, facing the water, stood the Eskimo huts built of driftwood, whalebone, or stones, chinked with dried turf and banked with snow—and here, after the whale hunt, the kill would be divided among the entire village. (It should be noted that the igloo, or snow house, was used more as a temporary dwelling while hunting or traveling than as a permanent abode.)

For the Aleuts, close relatives of the Eskimo, life in the cold dank reaches of southwestern Alaska was again little more than a matter of subsistence. Along the shores were the Aleut villages made up of driftwood or whalebone houses. Birds, fish, shellfish, and sea mammals, including the seal, the closely related sea lion, and the sea otter, were the principal foods. Among the low-growing vegetation of the treeless

Aleutians the native peoples found berries and other edible plant food.

When the Russians came upon the Aleutians in 1741, they brutally enslaved the natives, forcing them to hunt the sea otter for pelts. During the century that followed, both the unfortunate Aleuts and the sea otters were driven to a point nearing extermination by the ruthless practices of the Russian fur traders.

Today a promising sheep-raising industry has begun to flourish in the Aleutians. Although the weather is generally on the uncomfortably cool side on these islands, the moderating effect of the sea prevents extremes of winter cold and summer heat. Moist-climate grasses, herbs, and other greenery provide good grazing nearly twelve months a year, and the lack of sunshine is not an obstacle to healthy sheep growing. Some islands in the Aleutians have from five to six days of rain per week, and not even a dozen clear days in a year. But Aleutian sheep produce wool with strong, uniform fibers and minimal processing shrinkage, and Aleutian lamb chops are said to be unexcelled in flavor.

GOLD RUSH DAYS IN ALASKA

When the Russians pulled out of Alaska in 1867 due to the diminishing supply of furs, they little dreamed that thirteen years later the first of the big Alaska gold strikes would be made. The existence of rich mineral deposits in Alaska had, of course, long been a matter for speculation. But the Russian interest was chiefly in ready-made wealth, in the furs of foxes, beaver, mink, muskrat, seal, and sea otter.

In 1879 John Muir, the Scottish-American naturalist, visited the Alaska Panhandle to study glaciers. His hunch that there were gold deposits in the vicinity was acted upon by two miners from Sitka, and the following year the boom town of Juneau was born. The rush was on.

In 1896 came the discovery of the Klondike gold fields just over the Alaska border in Canada. Prospectors poured into this region and into eastern Alaska by the hundreds. Placer gold turned up in the form of valuable beach deposits on the Seward Peninsula in western Alaska in 1899. Here the town of Nome sprang into being, and from a crude mining camp soon bulged with a population of over twelve thousand. Fairbanks, in the interior, saw its gold rush beginning in 1902. So went the trek of the "sourdoughs" into the northland.

The cherished crock of sourdough starter, used for leavening biscuits, hot cakes, and the like, became the badge of the Alaskan gold prospector; and to this day, established non-native Alaskans, regardless of their business or profession, are tagged sourdoughs. (A newcomer to Alaska is a *cheechako*, derived from Chinook Indian jargon for "tenderfoot.")

A fermented mixture of sugar, flour, and water, or a few potatoes boiled and then left to ferment was usually the basis of the sourdough, a little of which was added to bread or biscuit dough before baking so that the results would be light and fluffy. Each time some of the sourdough starter was used, flour, salt, and lukewarm water were added to the crock as a replacement—and these soon became part of the bubbling, yeasty mixture. As in the old West and the Southwest, a sourdough mixture kept warm enough and properly replenished went on working for years.

Coffee, tea, flour, lard, bacon, and salt pork were the basic food supplies of the first sourdoughs. Throughout the Alaskan gold country, prices of food and other necessities were staggering. In the Nome gold rush, a serving of ham and eggs cost a dollar and a half, a great deal of money, and enough in those days to buy a really sumptuous meal in a fashionable New York restaurant. Almost all purchases were paid for in gold dust, and every store in town had scales for weighing out gold against purchses made. In the gold-town saloons, shootings, gambling, carousing, and heavy drinking prevailed. The year 1898, following on the great Klondike gold strike, saw a peak of lawlessness in the almost legendary Alaskan border town of Skagway, a jumping-off point for the Canadian gold fields.

Today Alaskan gold mining is no longer the profitable enterprise it once was. The price of gold is not high enough to justify the use of costly equipment and the high operating expenses it takes to dredge up gold in quantity. While large mining companies that are still taking gold out of Alaska do exist, it goes without saying that the individual prospector stands little chance against them. Like the furs that were once Alaska's chief source of wealth, gold, too, began to decline—and its place was taken by, of all things, fish.

EATING IN ALASKA TODAY

Fish, indeed, is the key to good eating in Alaska: grilled king salmon steak; cold cracked Dungeness crab; Alaskan king crab, dripping with butter. King crab is a spiny-shelled monster often measuring from four to six feet across, and weighing anywhere from eleven to over twenty pounds. Its delicate, pink-tinged white meat tastes about halfway between lobster and crab.

Alaskan fish specialties go on and on. There is broiled Dolly Varden, cutthroat, or rainbow trout, baked halibut (Alaskan halibut run to hundreds of pounds), succulent Alaskan shrimp, and the great white sheefish (also called the inconnu), a salmonlike delicacy that spawns in the Arctic rivers that empty into the Bering Sea and the Arctic Ocean.

In the autumn, reindeer comes to market in Alaska. Roasts, chops, and charcoal-broiled reindeer steaks are featured regional specialties. Game is a standby on Alaska menus. Moose and caribou, shot in season, are kept in freezer lockers to stretch into meals for the months ahead. Bear, if it is young and has eaten only berries and roots, makes a tasty offering. But older animals, particularly bears that have been eating dead fish and other carrion, do not have palatable flesh. Alaskan varieties of wild goose and duck are much prized.

Alaska's small but choice livestock industry sends to market chops and roasts from Aleutian lamb, tender well-marbled beef from herds raised on Kodiak Island and in the Matanuska Valley, and hams, sausages, and pork roasts from the growing number of pork farms in Alaska.

Of home-grown vegetables, the Alaskan potato appears to

be the coming challenge to Idaho, Maine, and New York's
Long Island. Alaska's fine mealy varieties yield top-quality
potato chips and French fries.

At Haines, near the top of the Panhandle, a strawberry
festival is held each year in July, just at berry-ripening time.
Here the teacup-sized beauties are displayed by the pailful,
so large and luscious that a single berry, sliced and laid on
a plate, makes a serving. Homemade strawberry preserves,
strawberry waffles, and strawberry shortcake are offered for
sale to the delight of visitors.

Traces of foreign cookery linger on in Alaska. The city
of Sitka, founded as a Russian trading post in 1799, became
during the nineteenth century the gay and brilliant center
of Russian America, as Alaska was then called. After the
United States bought Alaska in 1867, Sitka, which is situated
on an offshore island in the Panhandle, continued to serve
as capital until the mainland city of Juneau took over.

Today, Russian influences are still evident in Sitka, in her bulbous-steepled Russian Orthodox Church, in the Russian family names listed in her telephone book, in the Russian tea served in her homes. At Easter time Russian foods and customs prevail among many of Sitka's inhabitants, who bake *kulich,* the elaborate Russian Easter bread, and exchange handsomely decorated Easter eggs just as in old Russia.

Petersburg, also located in the Panhandle, offers yet another foreign flavor. Oddly enough, this town began neither as a Russian trading post nor as a gold town. It was established by Norwegian fishermen and remains to this day a typically Norwegian community, its economy based on fish, and secondarily, on logging. In May, Petersburg holds its spring festival in celebration of Norwegian Independence Day, the day on which Norway received her constitution. Norwegian costumes, traditional songs and dances, and a round of fish fries, salmon barbecues, and smorgasbord feasts typify this gay and colorful occasion.

Eskimo eating patterns, as we have seen, are presently in a state of flux. A dinner of raw whale steak may be topped off with a serving of canned peaches. Matters of both custom and convenience are involved. In many sections of the northland there is no flowing water, no electricity, and no wood or coal for fuel. Ice must be cut from the river bank and melted in order to brew tea or coffee or to cook a stew. Fuel oil, with the exception of local seal or whale oil, must be imported and is therefore costly, although it is hoped that the discovery of oil in Alaska in 1957 will eventually increase Alaska's fuel supply and lessen its cost.

Nevertheless many Eskimo foods are today served cooked. A modern Eskimo meal offered to a non-native visitor might consist of dried or smoked fish, reindeer stew, and a dessert

of fresh or preserved Arctic berries served with sugar and canned milk, or in the more traditional fashion, with seal oil. *Akutok,* the Eskimo "ice cream," is still quite popular, as is a similar concoction of cranberries and fish eggs, beaten to a fluff.

For the Alaskan resident, as opposed to the tourist, there is another side to the eating picture. This is the high cost of all foods shipped into Alaska from outside. Despite home-produced meats and agricultural products and the abundance of native fish, Alaska still imports a very large percentage of her meats, milk, and fresh produce and just about all her canned goods and other groceries.

While Alaska's growing season is long in hours of sunshine, it is short in number of days. "Out of season" is a long time, during which a head of lettuce flown in from California may come to sixty cents, and a stalk of celery to ninety. Likewise, fruits such as apples and bananas may cost from eighty cents to one dollar a pound. This is particularly true in Fairbanks and other cities of the interior, for freight and labor costs are high and Alaska has so few roads that many settlements can only be served by airplane on the final lap of delivery. Of course salaries in Alaska are generally higher to offset these increased living costs.

In summing up, what single regional food or dish can we point to as being exclusively Alaskan? Is it Alaskan king crab, Arctic sheefish or Eskimo *akutok*? Or is it a Fairbanks specialty that originated in early mining days—*pickled moose nose*? The recipe is simple. Scald a moose nose and pick off the hairs. Boil in water with onions, spices, and vinegar. Cool the moose nose in its juices, chill, and serve sliced!

Since the first salmon cannery was built in 1878, fish has been Alaska's most important food export. Most of Alaska's five principal commercial varieties of salmon wind up in cans, with Ketchikan in the lower Panhandle an important canning center. Halibut, cod, and herring, caught by Ketchi-

FOOD PRODUCTS OF ALASKA TODAY

kan fishing fleets, are also processed here. The young herring are frequently packed as sardines.

Fish freezing is an important Alaska industry, with millions of pounds processed in this way each year. Especially popular and now very widely available throughout the United States is Alaskan king crab, which is caught off Kodiak Island in southwestern Alaska. King crab is distributed both frozen and canned. An even newer export is the excellent Alaskan shrimp found in the waters off Kodiak Island. So plentiful and so easy to harvest are these delicious crustaceans that they have aroused both the envy and the interest of Louisiana shrimp packers.

While Alaska is well on her way in the home production of potatoes and other vegetables, grains, berries, meats, and dairy products, she is still on the receiving rather than distributing end where these foods are concerned. Her potential, however, is vast, and as improved roads and busier air routes shorten the distances from the northland, more of her food products will surely begin to see distribution beyond her state lines.

ALASKAN RECIPES
TO TRY

ALASKAN KING CRAB SAUTE

(2 servings)

1	6-ounce package frozen Alaskan king crab meat
2	tablespoons butter
½	teaspoon lemon juice
½	teaspoon Worcestershire sauce
½	teaspoon finely chopped fresh parsley

Defrost the crab meat and drain off all liquid that has accumulated. In a medium-small skillet melt the butter. Add the remaining ingredients and bring mixture to a sizzle. Add the crab meat, broken into large chunks, and toss about 3 minutes in the hot butter mixture. Transfer to a serving plate, pouring the remaining butter mixture from the pan over the crab meat. Sprinkle with additional lemon juice if desired. Good served with a baked potato and a cooked green vegetable or a salad.

BAKED ALASKAS

(6 servings)

4	egg whites
8	tablespoons sugar
6	spongecake dessert shells, about 3 inches in diameter, or spongecake layers cut into 3-inch rounds
1 to 1½	pints ice cream, frozen hard

Set oven for 450 degrees. Have egg whites at room temperature. Beat with a rotary beater or in an electric mixer until they are stiff enough to hold their shape in peaks. Add the sugar one tablespoon at a time, beating after each addition. Meringue should be shiny and very stiff.

Check oven to make sure it has reached 450 degrees. Place the 6 spongecakes on a cooky sheet or very shallow baking pan. Using an ice-cream scoop, place a generous mound of ice cream in the center of each dessert shell. (It is a good idea to have the dessert shells frozen, too, before using.) Cover quickly with enough meringue to coat *all* of the ice cream and the cake right down to the pan surface. Meringue should be about ¼ to ½ inch thick. Have surface slightly swirled. Place Alaskas in 450-degree oven and bake for about 4 minutes, or until meringue is a deep golden brown. Transfer to dessert plates and serve at once.

Baked Alaska was developed in honor of Alaska by Delmonico's, a fashionable New York restaurant, in 1867, the year the United States purchased that territory. The recipe is offered here in that same spirit, this time honoring Alaska's admission to the Union in 1959.

hawaii

From the ice of Alaska to the fire of Hawaii is but a few hours' flight by jet airplane. Yet the transition from the forty-ninth state to the fiftieth is not lightly made, for the two are an overwhelming study in contrasts.

Set in the midst of the world's largest ocean, over 2,000 miles from the nearest mainland, Hawaii remained for centuries unknown and unsuspected by the navigators of the Pacific. Sailing ships plowing their way across the ocean were far more likely to miss than to hit this chain of eight volcanic islands, their total land area smaller than that of the state of New Jersey.

Born on the floor of the great Pacific, the Hawaiian Islands were thrust upward by means of a series of undersea eruptions. Continuing relentlessly over tens of millions of years, such eruptions created build-ups of molten rock which emerged at last from the sea as steaming mountain tops. Black and barren, these mountains were the cores of the islands we know today. On the island of Hawaii, largest and most southeasterly of the group, volcanic action is still going on, a fiery spectacle that draws a steady stream of awestruck spectators.

Clearly, the Hawaiian Islands could not have chosen a better spot in which to be born. Like Sunday's child, they are endowed with all the blessings. Although their location in the Pacific places them in the tropic zone, they are spared the discomforts of tropical heat by cool ocean currents and by the trade winds that blow steadily out of the northeast. These winds bring rather heavy rainfall to the eastern slopes of the islands. On Kauai, at the northerly tip of the chain, as much as 51 *feet* (over 600 inches) of rain have been recorded in a single year. Lush flower, shrubbery, and tree growth on this side of Kauai has tagged it the Garden Island. Sugar cane grows well on Kauai, for this plant is so water-loving that it has been estimated that one ton of water is required to produce one pound of sugar.

On the westerly slopes of the islands, however, rainfall is much sparser, for the trade winds, cooled by the high peaks, have lost their moisture. Some areas receive as little as 10 inches of rainfall per year and will support only cacti and other low-moisture vegetation. In some westerly sections of the islands, fields must be artificially irrigated in order to grow crops. On the "big island" of Hawaii, dry grassy plains, reminiscent of the mainland's Western plains, support a gigantic cattle-ranching industry.

While there are extremes of wetness and dryness on the islands, the temperature is divinely even. Temperatures can, however, be varied at will. Climb the volcanic mountains of Mauna Kea or Mauna Loa in winter and the weather will grow steadily colder as you approach their snow-covered peaks. On the beaches below, however, it is still summer, with temperatures almost always hovering in the mid-seventies. In fact so generally even and pleasant is the climate of Hawaii that the native language has no word for weather. The conversation has never required one.

No wonder then that the masses of black volcanic rock, conditioned by wind, sun, rain, and waves, were gradually pulverized to fertile soil. True, life came slowly to these islands because of their great distance from other land masses. Plant and insect life must have reached the islands in the form of seeds or eggs carried by birds, wind currents, or floating debris. Those that could adapt to the soil and climate flourished and produced new varieties of their kind and even new species. Birds, of course, reached the islands with little difficulty, while fish and sea mammals circled their shores from the very beginning. The only mammal actually living *on* the Hawaiian Islands before the coming of man, however, was the bat.

The Polynesians, who began arriving in Hawaii about two thousand years before the Pilgrims disembarked at Plymouth Rock, were a good deal better prepared for settlement than were their English counterparts. They even seemed to have a clearer idea of where they were going, of the soil and climate conditions of their new land.

THE FOODS AND COOKERY OF THE FIRST HAWAIIANS

All of this seems impossible in view of the Stone Age culture and the generally primitive background of these people. From their island homes in Samoa and other archipelagos that lay to the south and the west of Hawaii was a distance of more than 2,000 miles across open seas. The Polynesians had no knowledge of metals, no written language, and therefore no charts and probably no navigational instruments to help them find their way. But they were magnificent seafarers. Their studies of winds and currents, of the stars and of the flight of birds, guided them, in their wonderfully balanced double-hulled canoes, to the distant new islands.

Voyages and migrations to nearer islands warned the Polynesians that even a green Pacific isle could be woefully lacking in the foods they liked best to eat. Thus they were careful to stock their large open boats with enough provisions, not only to last throughout the journey, but also to insure a continuing supply of plant and animal foods once ashore.

To this end, the Polynesians brought to Hawaii roots and slips or seedlings of such plants as taro (from which their well-loved *poi* was made), banana, plantain (the cooking banana), breadfruit (a bland-fleshed globe, also eaten cooked), yam, coconut, and sugar cane which they had no way of processing but loved to chew on raw. They also took the trouble to bring along roots of the plant from which the Samoan ceremonial drink *kava* was made.

To prepare this drink it was the custom for young boys and girls with strong teeth to chew on the leaves of the plant until well mashed. The roots were also pounded and used. Then water and coconut milk were added to the leaf-and-root mash, and the brew was left to ferment. It was drunk lukewarm from coconut shells. Although not so prevalent in Hawaii today, *kava* may still be readily sampled by the curious in Fiji and Samoa.

Lastly, the Polynesians brought along their three favorite animals—pigs, chickens, and dogs—in sufficient breeding pairs to guarantee future generations. The dogs were not taken along on the ride for companionship, but were meat to the Polynesians, who, like many of the North American Indians, made it a regular practice to eat dogs.

Polynesian food, whenever it is mentioned today, calls to mind a mouth-watering cuisine composed of savory tidbits, crisp succulent meats, luscious seafoods, and flower-fragrant

fruits dripping with honeyed juice. To equate these modern Polynesian delights with those of old Hawaii would be erroneous. The early Hawaiians had a menu pretty much limited to the foods they brought with them from their previous island homes, and supplemented with fish and edible seaweeds from local waters.

Onions, garlic, soy sauce, lemon juice, and many kinds of spices were unknown. Meats such as beef and domesticated duckling did not, of course, exist, and there was no game on the islands at all. Papayas, mangoes, citrus fruits, avocados, and the very pineapple so closely associated with Hawaii were yet to be introduced.

The early Hawaiians grew no wheat, corn, rice, or other grain. Poi was their "bread," although it was eaten in the form of a thick pasty pudding. No regular mealtimes were observed in old Hawaii. When food was plentiful, eating simply went on more or less continuously all day. When food was scarce, everyone fasted. It would therefore be inaccurate to say that poi, like bread, was eaten three times a day. It was eaten *throughout* the day, with some of the heartier appetites consuming as much as 18 pounds of poi in a single twenty-four-hour period!

Poi is prepared from the root of the taro, a water-loving lilylike plant with pointed heart-shaped leaves. The leaves also serve as food, and are a little like spinach when cooked. The root of the taro is thick and fleshy, and when Mark Twain visited Hawaii in 1866 he called taro the "corpulent sweet potato." By tradition, it was the men of Hawaii who pounded the purplish-brown taro root (after it had first been baked and peeled) into poi. A squat stone pestle and large saucer-shaped wooden mortar were the implements used. As the pounding continued, a little water was added until the mixture resembled bread dough, except of course for its lavender color.

The poi was then stored in gourds or other vessels. It was mixed with a little more water at serving time, and was eaten with the fingers, for tableware was unknown to the early Hawaiians. The method for eating poi was to dip one finger into the mixture and quickly scoop up a mouthful. If the poi was a bit thin, two fingers would be used. For a poi that tended to be on the drippy side, three fingers were required. Thus the designations one-finger poi, two-finger poi, and three-finger poi were a key to the consistency of the dish.

Legend has it that poi originated when an ancient king grew so tired of eating plain baked taro root that he pounded it with his fists and flung it aside in disgust. The pulpy mixture began to ferment. Out of curiosity, someone, perhaps the king himself, tasted the mashed taro and declared that it now had a most delicious flavor. Few non-native Hawaiians will agree. Poi is basically bland with a slightly sour tang due to fermentation. Native Hawaiians, however, still consume so much poi that it is today prepared commercially on the islands.

Plantain and breadfruit are also starchy and nourishing, but not very interestingly flavored foods. The plantain looks like a large green banana and is inedible until cooked. Breadfruit, so named because its raw pulp somewhat resembles the consistency of fresh bread, is also greenish-skinned and about the size and shape of a child's head. It, too, must be baked before eating. Yams, similar to the sweet potato but sweeter and deeper in color, were a bit tastier than the other basic Hawaiian foods, but were also of a waxy, starchy texture.

It is no wonder, therefore, that the early Hawaiians grew fat. Indeed, stoutness was a mark of high status. Great physical girth meant that one was wealthy and powerful enough to be indolent and could therefore indulge in constant eating. Many ancient Hawaiian rulers weighed 400 pounds or more. Like the common people, Hawaiian kings, queens, and chieftains ate with their fingers, dipping up poi, tearing away with their teeth at raw squid or steamed pork, and washing the food down with great gulps of coconut milk. Royalty, however, made it a practice to eat lying on their stomachs rather than squatting on the ground. When a king or queen had reached a point where he or she could eat no more, an agile servant simply rolled the monarch over on his back and massaged and pounded his abdomen until his appetite returned.

Cooking methods were very limited in old Hawaii, for there were no metals and the Hawaiians made no pottery. They did, however, do some stone-boiling, using gourds or hollowed-out wooden vessels. Like many of the North American tribes, the Hawaiians simply heated stones in the fire and then dropped them into the stew pot to bring the water

to boiling and cook whatever foods—fish, chicken, yams, taro leaves—had been added to it.

More popular as a cooking device was the underground oven, or *imu* (pronounced ee-moo). A pit was dug in the ground and lined with kindling wood and with stones that had special heat-retentive qualities. Then a fire was laid in the pit to heat the stones thoroughly. The food, wrapped in large banana or *ti* palm leaves, was then placed in the pit to cook. Water-soaked mats and more leaves covered the top of the *imu* to keep the food within continuously steaming. This method is very similar to that of the New England clambake where damp sand and seaweed, the cornhusks and the clam and lobster shells, all serve to keep the food cooking in moist heat.

Whole pigs, chickens, and dogs were thus cooked by the early Hawaiians, as well as birds, fish, and vegetables. It is a mistake, however, to visualize a baked pig emerging from the *imu* browned and crisp-skinned, like a Thanksgiving turkey. *Imu* meats, fish, and poultry were cooked by a steaming rather than a roasting process. They had literally been "boiled" in their own juices and, although they were highly nutritious, their flavor left much to be desired in terms of contemporary Western tastes.

The early Hawaiians, however, feasted happily on these foods. They made no distinction between hot and cold foods, or between what we would call breakfast, luncheon, or dinner dishes. Thus the cooked contents of the *imu* would be eaten at air temperature for as long as they lasted, and a bit of pig or fish or yam was as good for a meal on arising in the morning as it had been the previous evening before going to sleep. Taro root, for making poi, was baked *imu* fashion. So were breadfruit and yams, from which a poi could also be prepared. Baking time was slow for these vegetables, generally three to four hours, but time was an ever-present commodity on the islands.

Gourds, coconut shells, and hollowed-out bowls of wood or stone were used as drinking vessels and serving dishes. *Ti* leaves or banana leaves served as plate and place mat in one. All foods were taken, of course, with the fingers.

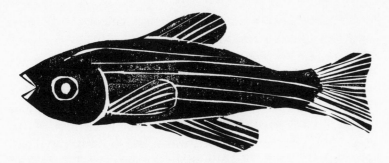

Fish were the principal "game" of the early Hawaiians. Mullet was so great a favorite that they were penned off into separate ponds where they could breed unmolested and be taken from the water when desired, or when other foods were scarce. There are so many varieties of fish in Hawaiian waters that it has been said a modern-day tourist could eat a different fish for breakfast each day for weeks and still not have tasted them all. Netting, spearing, hooking, and trapping (in slatted wooden cages not unlike the New England lobster traps) were some of the fishing methods used. Nor was hand-to-hand grappling with octopus and squid (a ten-armed member of the octopus family) shunned by these intrepid fishermen. Dolphin, tuna, pink snapper, barracuda, and a great many varieties that still bear only native names were food for the early Hawaiians. In addition lobsters, crabs, shrimp, *opihi* (small black clamlike shellfish), and turtles abounded on or near the island shores. Small fish were sometimes eaten raw on the spot as they were caught, but larger fish were usually taken ashore to be steam-baked in the *imu*. The early Hawaiians also salted and dried fish for preservation, and as there were no metals on the islands to serve as money, salted fish was used as a medium of exchange.

As was true in many other cultures, the early Hawaiians observed a set of taboos relating to cookery and diet. Women, for example, were not permitted to eat pork, turtles, bananas, coconuts, or certain varieties of fish. Nor were they allowed to cook these foods. Perhaps the purpose of this second taboo was to keep the women from being tempted to nibble on the forbidden delicacies while preparing them.

In addition men and women were not permitted to eat

together or even to cook their foods in the same oven. While
the men might sit on the ground while eating, the women
generally carried small vessels of food around with them, eating as they moved about to do their tasks. The men were favored with the choicer and rarer foods; recognizing the man's
vital function in their economy, the women accepted this.

Like all taboos, however, the dietary restrictions of the
early Hawaiians were doomed once the necessity for them
had passed. At last, in 1819 (some forty years after Captain
Cook's visit, which marked the opening of the islands to the
outside world) the Hawaiian king Liholiho sat down to dine
with the dowager queen at a public feast, thus putting an
end to one of the basic taboos of the ancient Hawaiians.

*FROM CAPTAIN COOK
TO THE HAWAIIAN
MELTING POT*

The search for a water route across North America that
would link the Atlantic and Pacific oceans was still going
on at the time of the American Revolution. The English
explorer Captain James Cook was bent on just such a mission when he sighted a group of uncharted Pacific islands
in January of 1778.

It is difficult to say which of the parties involved was more
surprised by the ensuing landing—the Hawaiian natives, or
Cook along with the officers and crews of his two ships, the
Resolution and the aptly named *Discovery*. In any case, the
Hawaiian Islands (which Cook named the Sandwich Islands
in honor of his patron, the English Earl of Sandwich) were
never to be the same again.

The Hawaiians, who knew only their own canoes of native
koa wood, had difficulty at first in recognizing the masted
English vessels as ships. They were able to think of them
only as floating bits of land, comparable in some way to their
own islands. Even more shocking to the natives was the
abundance of metals both on board ship and on the persons
of the sailors themselves. The Hawaiians had, in the past,
pried bits of metal loose from occasional pieces of driftwood,
the wave-tossed remnants of some distant sea wreck. But here
was a profusion of objects from buttons and buckles to

anchors and anvils. The natives were fascinated and lured by the strong, clanging substance that could be fashioned in so many ways, and was particularly useful for hooks, spears, and other fishing gear. Thus, for a single iron nail the Hawaiians cheerfully supplied an entire ship's company with a day's eating of fish, pork, yams, and poi.

Of further interest to the Hawaiians were the foods that the English sailors customarily ate aboard ship. These were mainly salt beef and ship's biscuit, which was appropriately known as hardtack. Both foods were almost as tough as the nails that the Hawaiians so highly prized, but they provided the natives with their first taste of beef and of a bread product prepared from wheat flour. Of the foods traded during that first visit, the English sailors undoubtedly got the better of the bargain. The Hawaiians, however, stubbornly continued to regard these eighteenth-century ships' provisions as delicacies.

Misunderstandings revolving around the islanders' desire for metal objects led to brief hostilities on Captain Cook's return visit the following winter. Cook was unfortunately killed in a skirmish with the Hawaiians, but his role in revealing the Hawaiian Islands to the world was an important one. A monument on the west coast of the island of Hawaii marks the spot where he met his death.

Among the officers in Captain Cook's party was George Vancouver, a young midshipman who returned to the islands in 1792 in charge of his own expedition. He introduced a number of plants and trees, and returned the following year with a gift of Spanish longhorn cattle from California, the first examples of beef on the hoof that the Hawaiians had ever seen.

At the direction of the Hawaiian king Kamehameha, no cattle from the herd which Vancouver brought were to be slaughtered for a period of ten years. While the king's foresight in allowing the herd to multiply was commendable, the wild Spanish cattle throve so well on the rich grassland slopes of Hawaii island's Mauna Kea that they were soon terrorizing the local population and destroying crops. In the 1830s, while the American West was still very young, Mexican cowboys were brought to Hawaii to teach their arts to

the natives. The first horses had been brought to Hawaii in 1803, and roping and roundups, branding and penning, were soon in progress in the Hawaiian cattle country. To this day the Hawaiian cowboy rides in a Mexican saddle and calls himself a *paniolo,* derived from the Spanish spoken by his Mexican tutors.

The Spanish were also responsible for popularizing the fruit that is today most closely associated with Hawaii. The pineapple was native to tropical America and is thought to have been brought back to Spain as early as 1493 by Columbus. It caused a sensation in Europe, and because it had to be carefully grown in hothouses, it soon became known as the "fruit of kings." Spanish sailors may have brought the first planting slips to Hawaii, but it was a Spanish horticulturist, Francisco de Paula y Marín, who really began to cultivate this fruit on the islands some time between 1800 and 1820.

Marín also grew oranges, grapes, figs, roses, and many kinds of vegetables. He is credited with the introduction into Hawaii of the mango (a peachlike tropical fruit) and the avocado, both transplanted from Mexico. Today, trees of both these fruits flourish in many Hawaiian back yards. Marín also kept a herd of cattle, and in addition to salting beef, he popularized milk, butter, and cream, previously unknown on the islands.

Today the island of Lanai is known as the Pineapple Island. Almost completely company-owned, it is devoted chiefly to the growing and processing of pineapples. Most of the other islands also produce quantities of this fruit. Pineapples are usually planted not from seed, but from slips, suckers, or crowns which are laid into the soil through strips of paper punched with holes. The paper strips serve as a mulch, keeping the soil moist and preventing weeds from growing up around the young plants.

Pineapple plants require about two years to mature, during which time their paper collars disintegrate and their spectacular leaf growth brings them to a height of nearly four feet. It is said that fresh pineapple eaten anywhere but in a Hawaiian pineapple field is not a pineapple at all, no matter how sweet the taste. For fruit to be shipped fresh, pineapple is picked green and allowed to ripen slowly en route. But a sun-ripened fresh pineapple provides a never-to-be-forgotten eating experience—nectar-sweet with no trace of unpleasant acidity, and a color so richly golden you can almost taste the sunshine.

The voyages of Captain Cook had indeed wrought great changes in Hawaii. The islands were a convenient stopping place, and soon trading ships and whalers were calling regularly. The first missionaries, a Protestant group from New England, arrived in 1820. The islands had recently been united under a single ruler, King Kamehameha I. In the previous year, the taboos slowly began to be abolished, and now, along with missionary schools and churches, the New Englanders introduced more foods of the Western world to Hawaii, particularly vegetables, grains, and livestock.

Samuel Ruggles, also a missionary, planted the first coffee trees on the Kona coast of the island of Hawaii in 1828. By 1850 there were coffee plantations on several of the islands, and it was Hawaiian coffee that was shipped to the mainland and sold to the California miners during the gold rush years. Today Hawaiian coffee is again being grown chiefly in the Kona region and is exported for use in blends, to which it adds its own special flavor.

Of all the rich products of Hawaii's soil and climate, sugar cane has been the most influential in changing life on the islands. It was sugar that brought American planters to Hawaii, sugar that imported the Chinese, Portuguese, Japanese, and Filipino cane fieldworkers who in turn changed the composition of the Hawaiian population. It was sugar that led to the movement for United States annexation (a means of removing the tariff that country had imposed on Hawaiian sugar), and sugar that led indirectly to statehood for Hawaii in 1959.

Sugar cane is not native to Hawaii, but it seems as natural to these tropical islands as apple trees now do to New England. The Polynesians had brought this sweet-tasting member of the grass family along with them in their canoes from their island homes to the south. Once ashore in Hawaii they planted the cane as fencing for their taro patches. When Captain Cook visited Hawaii in 1778, he found sugar cane growing freely and observed that the islanders were in the habit of chewing on the stalks for their flavor.

Americans built the first sugar mill on Kauai Island in 1835 and then waited for a crop to be ready for processing. Sugar cane is planted from cuttings rather than from seed, and like pineapple takes about two years to mature. Extensive moisture is vital, and most fields have to be irrigated. The first crude milling, a crushing process followed by heating and filtering the juice, yielded two tons of sugar, a poor result for the quantity of cane processed. Modern equipment cuts the cane into short lengths and then presses out every last droplet of juice. The dried-out bits of cane can be used for fuel or are sometimes pressed into wallboard. Sugar is not refined on the islands into the crystalline white substance with which we are most familiar. It is shipped to California in the form of raw sugar, moist brown lumps that have a pleasant molasses-like flavor, but that few people ever get to taste.

A most interesting aspect of sugar harvesting is the burning over of the fields. To one unfamiliar with this practice, the sight is a rather terrifying one, for the air is filled with the smell of burning candy and it appears that an entire two years' harvest is about to be lost. In fact the origin of this custom is said to have been an accidental fire which appeared to have destroyed a good part of a sugar plantation before it could be controlled. Close examination after the fire, however, revealed that the cane itself was undamaged, while the leaves and other waste that encumbered the 6-to-12-foot stalks had been burned away, making harvesting much easier. Today cane-field burning is standard practice in Hawaii.

The sugar industry began to grow rapidly in the mid-nineteenth century. The California gold rush and the subsequent settling of the West created a new and demanding market for island sugar. New fields were laid out, the cane sprang up, but the small native labor force was not particularly interested in doing tedious and backbreaking work on the vast sugar plantations.

Thus the plantation owners turned to other labor markets. Chinese workers were brought to Hawaii, and a little later,

Portuguese workers from the cane-producing Azores. These were followed in the 1880s by the largest foreign group to date, the Japanese, and still later by the Filipinos. Many other national groups—French, German, English, Irish, Korean, Mexican—have filtered into Hawaii over the years, making her the most truly integrated and racially harmonious of all her sister states. Indeed, Hawaii has been called "the melting pot" in the strictest democratic sense. She is also a culinary melting pot, for she encompasses a fascinating collection of native and imported cuisines that make eating in modern Hawaii an almost international experience.

Lomi lomi, pipikuala, and taro cakes all sound like, and are today perfectly legitimate Hawaiian dishes. Yet the early Hawaiians would not have known what to make of them. None of these foods could have been prepared on the islands in pre-Captain Cook days.

EATING IN HAWAII TODAY

Lomi lomi, for example, is raw salted salmon, rubbed with a mixture of non-native ingredients such as chopped onions and tomatoes. *Pipikuala* is the Hawaiian version of jerked beef, salted and dried and sometimes served as a side dish at modern-day *luaus*. (Beef was, of course, unknown at the *luau* feasts of the early Hawaiians.) Taro cakes were another impossibility. While the basic ingredient of taro root was native in old Hawaii, these toothsome little fried cakes, crisp on the outside, tender on the inside, could not have been produced before the introduction of metal frying pans and deep-fat frying kettles from the outside world.

The modern Hawaiian restaurant's specialty of breast of chicken in pineapple shell, and the modern practice of seasoning the *luau* pig by rubbing it well with soy sauce before baking in the *imu,* are both the results of imported food touches. For pineapple the Hawaiians are indebted to the Spanish; for soy sauce, to the Orientals.

Older traditional dishes do, however, persist in modern Hawaii—chicken or *mahimahi* (dolphin) baked with taro tops in coconut milk, *limu* (dried seaweed, often used to garnish such dishes), and *lau laus* (pork, butterfish, and taro tops, neatly wrapped in *ti* leaves and steam-baked *imu* fashion). *Haupia* (taro-and-coconut pudding) is still the authentic island dessert. Breadfruit is sometimes substituted for the taro in this pudding.

Modern preferences, however, have resulted in such desserts as coconut and macadamia-nut ice creams, and papaya, passion fruit, and guava sherbets. The macadamia, native to Australia, is a delicately flavored nut about the size and shape of a cherry. Groves of macadamia trees are cultivated on the islands, for the nuts are used extensively both locally and for export. The unusual papaya, sometimes called the "tree melon," is popular in desserts and also as a breakfast fruit or juice in Hawaii. Its dark-green skin ripens to a high yellow, its meat is orange-red dotted with spicy seeds that add superb tang to a bite of the peach-sweet flesh. Passion fruit makes a luscious chiffon pie. Guavas are made into jams and marmalades, often combined with papaya or pineapple.

The pomelo is a pine-scented, citruslike fruit, larger, sweeter, and less juicy than grapefruit. All of these fruits, with the exception of the coconut, were unknown to the early Hawaiians, yet they flourish notably on the islands today and are very much a part of good eating in modern Hawaii.

Of the foreign populations in Hawaii, the large Japanese element exerts a powerful culinary influence. Japanese *sashimi* (thinly sliced raw fish) is a regular among the *puu puus,* or appetizers, served at Hawaiian dinners. If the idea of eating raw fish seems rather unpleasant, it is well to remember that people of the Western world have been eating raw clams and oysters for centuries and thinking nothing of it. *Sashimi* is usually served with soy sauce and may be curled around a dab of finely shredded turnip.

Another popular Japanese dish on the islands is the steaming noodle soup (sometimes served with floating bits of pork and green onion) known as *saimin.* This soup is sold at very informal sidewalk eating stands in Hawaii, much as pizzas or enchiladas are sold in various parts of the mainland.

Saimin makes a good inexpensive pick-me-up lunch for tourist or workingman. Its base is generally a mixture of shrimp, chicken, and seaweed stock. Well liked, too, are the delicate Japanese rice balls called *sushi*, sold at food bars. *Sushi,* which may be variously flavored, are dipped in soy sauce before being popped into the mouth. Wet towels are passed for wiping the fingers.

Shrimp or other foods prepared *tempura* style (batter-dipped and fried in deep fat), *teriyaki* (sliced beef soaked in soy sauce and then broiled), and *sukiyaki* (thin strips of beef and Oriental vegetables cooked to order) are other well-known Japanese specialties that are frequently encountered in Hawaii. Beef *hekka* is a beef-and-vegetable dish similar to *sukiyaki* that is very popular in the islands. Japanese pickled vegetables are commonly served with these dishes.

Rice is cultivated on Kauai Island by Japanese fieldworkers. The crop is not a large one, however, for primitive hand-planting and hand-harvesting methods are used, and the market is local. Most of the rice used in the Oriental cuisines of Hawaii is imported from the American mainland.

The Chinese have contributed ginger, litchi nuts, Canton duck, and tender little meat-stuffed dumplings to the cuisine of the islands. At Chinese restaurants in Hawaii, bird's-nest soup and shark's-fin soup may be sampled, along with dozens of better-known Chinese specialties. Shark's-fin soup is a chicken broth that actually contains dehydrated shark fins. But bird's-nest soup includes only the gum or saliva that swallows produce to hold their nests together and fasten them to their resting places. The gum is considered a delicacy by the Chinese, who gather it to be used as flavoring and thickening in this chicken-based soup. The nests themselves are omitted from the dish!

Fresh litchi nuts have been cultivated by the Chinese in Hawaii since 1873. Native to South China, the litchi is actually a fruit with white grapelike flesh and a most exotic perfumed flavor. The dark, prunelike dried litchi nuts that Westerners often sample are as different from the fresh litchis as raisins are from grapes. Litchis may be bought preserved in sirup and canned, but the tree-ripe litchi nuts of Hawaii are by far the most delicious.

A word must be said about Korean food, which is not generally known outside its homeland. The Korean population of the islands has supplied Hawaiian supermarkets and restaurants with samples of its cuisine, particularly the pepper-hot *kim chee* which translates into "merged vegetables." Put up in jars for sale in groceries or served in homes and restaurants out of crocks, *kim chee* is a pickled salad of cabbage, onions, celery, and turnips, strongly seasoned with garlic and hot red peppers. Non-Koreans are warned that powerful horseradish is as mild as milk compared with this fiery concoction!

Koreans are also recognized for their *kook soo,* a delicious pork broth with noodles, and their *mun doo,* delicate dumplings filled with "a thousand things," including chopped meats and water chestnuts, and often served in soup.

The list of food imports goes on and on. The Filipinos and the Portuguese have brought Hawaii their spicy pork sausages. From India have come an assortment of curries and a superb variety of mango. Introduced to Hawaii for cultivation in 1899, this fruit, non-fibrous and of a melting sweetness, is considered superior to the mango variety popularized earlier by Francisco de Paula y Marín. In fact, so bursting with juice is the Indian mango that the advice has often been given that it be eaten in the bathtub.

From Tahiti and other islands of the South Seas comes still another version of raw fish, this one marinated in lemon or lime juice and usually served with a sauce of coconut cream. The origin of lemon-marinated fish is uncertain. Citrus fruits were unknown in the islands of the South Seas, just as they were in Hawaii, until introduced by Europeans. To call this fish "raw," however, is somewhat inaccurate, for the acid of the lemon or lime juice actually "cooks" the fish until it is white and firm. Chopped onions or scallions may be added to the citrus marinade. The coconut cream served with the fish is a rich extract pressed from finely grated coconut meat, thicker and more flavorful than coconut milk. Coconut cream, a native Hawaiian ingredient, is used on the islands in Indian curries as well as on fresh cut-up fruits for which it makes an elegant dessert sauce.

Perhaps the most bizarre combination of ingredients to be encountered on the islands is that of a French-Hawaiian dish known as *mahimahi Veronique*. This international specialty consists of dolphin from Hawaiian waters cooked in the French manner with white wine, mushrooms, and seedless green grapes. Even more "United Nations" than this, perhaps, is a very American-style club sandwich of bacon, *mahimahi,* and sliced mango. How international can a cuisine get? No more so, surely, than in the fiftieth state.

HAWAII'S FEASTS AND FESTIVALS

A favorable climate year-round and an abundance of racial and religious groups make Hawaii the natural background for frequent holidays and outdoor festivities.

Hawaii's Japanese population celebrates a Cherry Blossom Festival, a Boy's Day (to honor sons), a Girl's Day (to collect heirloom dolls for daughters), and the popular Bon Dances, which began centuries ago to honor the dead and are today a community function featuring drummers and kimono-clad dancers. The Chinese of Hawaii hold a Narcissus Festival, which includes parades, beauty contests, and a Mandarin banquet, and their autumn Moon Festival, with its display of food offerings to the Moon Goddess. In Chinese shops round moon cakes, filled with chopped meats, are sold to be eaten at family feasts. Filipinos have a Filipino Festival in June and, particularly in the sugar-plantation villages, celebrate Rizal Day in December, in commemoration of the hero of Philippine Independence. Both are colorful holidays with traditional dances, and feasts that include roast pig and other Philippine national dishes.

Christmas, Easter, and Bodhi Day (which marks the beginning of Buddhism) are each welcomed with fervor in Hawaii. The Fourth of July brings on firecrackers and outrigger-canoe races, and Thanksgiving means a turkey dinner, even beneath the coconut palms.

The most Hawaiian of the holidays, however, are Lei Day on May 1, Kamehameha Day on June 11 (in honor of the king who first united the islands), and Aloha Week which falls in October. Aloha Week celebrates the spirit of the islands, the warmth, good humor, and tolerance of her people. All of these holidays bring on balls, hula dancing, parades, and of course an endless succession of *luaus*.

The *luau* feast is as old as the Hawaii of the first Polynesian settlers. In a sense it is the Thanksgiving of the islands, a feast to celebrate the bounty of the land and of the sea. Even the commercial *luau,* prepared for tourist groups in modern-day Hawaii, follows pretty much in the ancient cooking traditions.

The *luau* pig, skinned, scrubbed, and cleaned in preparation for the *imu,* is first well rubbed inside and out with Hawaiian rock salt and with the Oriental-derived soy sauce. Then red-hot *imu* stones are shoved into the body cavities so that cooking will take place from within as well as without. The front and back legs are now tied together. A cradle or hammock of wire-mesh screening serves to lower the pig into the leaf-lined *imu* and to keep the tender flesh from falling apart once the cooking is completed.

Yams, plantains, and *lau laus* are neatly tucked in around the pig. Leaves, wet burlap, and a blanket of dampened earth keep the steam from escaping while the food cooks for at least four to five hours in the *imu.* Like New Englanders waiting for a clambake to produce its succulent eatables, Hawaiians and visitors pass the time swimming, surfing, or just prowling the beaches and nearby points of interest. The great moment is the uncovering of the *imu,* the skillful removal of the hot stones, and the presentation and carving of the steamed pig, juicy, tender, and fragrant.

Luau accompaniments vary, but will nearly always include the *imu*-baked yams, plantains, and *lau laus,* and a serving of poi. Other side dishes at modern *luaus* are likely to be *opihi, lomi lomi,* chicken *luau* (baked with taro tops and coconut milk or coconut cream), and *pipikuala.* Garnishes usually include *limu* (seaweed), some Hawaiian rock salt, and chopped roasted *kukui* nuts (from the native-grown *kukui,* or candlenut tree). For dessert, a helping of *haupia,* or coconut and taro pudding. Is it any wonder the early Hawaiians tipped the scales at four hundred pounds!

Raw sugar and pineapple are, of course, Hawaii's most vital exports. The canning of pineapple goes back to the 1890s when increasing attempts to ship fresh pineapples to the American mainland met with heavy losses due to spoilage. Today pineapple harvesting is highly mechanized, and the canning of pineapple is a leading industry. Hawaii's canned pineapple products include slices, chunks, tidbits, spears, crushed fruit, and vast quantities of pineapple juice. Fresh pineapple, picked green, is also exported under improved shipping conditions, and most recently luscious field-ripened pineapples, flown to the mainland by jet aircraft, have appeared in luxury markets in the larger cities.

Coffee, which ranks third among Hawaii's agricultural products, is a much smaller but nevertheless substantial export.

Among special items are such Hawaiian food products as coconut sirup, dried salted coconut chips, guava preserves (sometimes in combination with fruits such as pineapple or papaya), and roasted salted macadamia nuts. These last are expensive but unusually delicious. All of these food specialties are to be found on the mainland chiefly in fancy groceries or in the delicacy departments of supermarkets and department stores.

HAWAIIAN FOOD EXPORTS

HAWAIIAN PINEAPPLE CHICKEN

(4 servings)

A HAWAIIAN RECIPE TO TRY

1 2¼- to 2½-pound broiling chicken, cut into eighths
   Salt
   Pepper

	Ground ginger
	Flour
2	tablespoons butter or margarine
1	medium onion, cut fine
1	cup chicken stock or 2 chicken-bouillon cubes dissolved in 1 cup boiling water
¼	cup diced green pepper (¼-inch pieces)
1	cup drained pineapple tidbits or drained pineapple chunks, cut in halves (save liquid)
1½	tablespoons cornstarch
2	tablespoons pineapple juice
1½	teaspoons soy sauce
1½	tablespoons brown sugar

Wash chicken pieces well and dry thoroughly. Sprinkle with salt, pepper, and ground ginger on all sides. Dust very lightly with flour. In a large skillet melt 1 tablespoon of the butter or margarine to sizzling. Add the chicken pieces in a single layer, skin side down, and cook to a pale golden brown. (It is important to use a deep skillet or a chicken fryer that has a cover.) Turn the chicken pieces and brown the other side lightly. Remove all browned chicken pieces and set aside.

Add the second tablespoon of butter to the skillet. Add the onion and sauté (fry) just until golden. Add the chicken stock or bouillon and blend it well with the pan scrapings. Add the chicken pieces, cover skillet, and cook over low heat about 25 minutes, or until chicken is tender. Carefully remove chicken pieces. Add the diced green pepper and the pineapple. Blend the cornstarch and pineapple juice until smooth. Add to skillet. Add soy sauce and brown sugar. Bring mixture to a boil, stirring constantly until sauce is clear and thickened. This will take about a minute. Return chicken pieces, heat through, and serve.

While this is certainly a modern rather than a traditional Hawaiian dish, it includes many valid Hawaiian ingredients and proves how well the flavors of chicken and pineapple marry. To keep the mood of the meal authentically Hawaiian, serve Pineapple Chicken with baked yams or sweet potatoes and a cooked green vegetable such as spinach.

index

(Asterisks after page numbers refer to recipes)

abalone, 232, 237
akutok, 251, 257
albondigas soup, 195
ale, in early New England, 38
Aleuts, 246, 247, 251–52
alewife, 45
almond, 194, 235, 237
anadama bread, 31
angel-food cake, 163, 164, 181
anijsmelk, 168
antelope, as game animal, 190, 203
apfel kuchen, 171
appelgebak, 168
apple butter, 79–80, 159
apple crops, 47, 89, 91, 92, 93, 140, 182, 183, 184, 234, 235, 236, 237
apple pandowdy, 15, 41
apple pie, Vermont, 40
apple slump, 40
applesauce, with baked beans, 26
Appleseed, Johnny, 158, 159
apricot, 193, 194, 226, 234, 235, 237
aquavit, 174
arroz con pollo, 198
artichoke, 233, 237
asparagus, 91, 93, 237
avocado, 141, 194, 199, 206, 232–33, 237, 267, 274

bacon, 124, 228, 253
baked Alaska, 87–88, 259*
banana, 265, 271
barbecue, 189, 205–6
barley, 22, 31, 38, 61, 62, 126, 183
bass, 91, 104, 151, 166, 183
bean soup, 86, 93–94*, 167
beans, 22, 56, 149, 152, 157, 167,

172, 182, 190, 194, 203, 204, 226, 234, 237; baked, 15, 25–26, 30, 157, 162
bear, as game animal, 16, 23, 59, 102, 125, 152, 156, 190, 214, 248, 254
beef, 33, 34, 76, 125, 141, 157, 182, 183, 195, 206, 211, 234, 254, 277, 279
beer, 38, 65, 69, 117, 126, 171–72, 174
beet, 34, 172, 181, 183, 234, 235
benne seeds, 120
berry soup, 167, 168
bighorn sheep, as game animal, 214
bird's-nest soup, 279
biscuit: beaten, 111–12; sourdough, 202–3
blackberry, 20, 59, 101, 126, 151, 168, 223, 236
blackberry flummery, 40, 41
blackberry jam, 130
blue crab, 56, 83, 87, 93
blueberry, 20, 91, 182, 250
blueberry grunt, 40
boova shenkel, 76, 77
Boston cream pie, 41–42
bouillabaisse, 134–35, 232
brandy, 67, 69, 117
breadfruit, 265, 269, 270, 278
bream, 104
brioche, 136
broccoli, 233, 237
brown bread, 15, 26
Brunswick stew, 114, 127
Brussels sprouts, 237
buckwheat, 61, 89, 91
buffalo, 59, 147, 152, 153, 154, 155, 190, 203, 214, 219

bun, Philadelphia sticky, 73–74
burgoo, 127
butter, 64, 183
buttermilk, 65
butternut, 20, 59, 151

cabbage, 48, 157, 245–46, 255
cacao bean, 193, 199
café au lait and *café brûlot,* 137
calas, 136
camass, 216
Camembert cheese, 182
cantaloupe, 92–93, 141, 206, 207, 235
Canton duck, 279
canvasback duck, 152, 164
Cape Cod turkey, 28
caribou, as game animal, 243, 248, 249, 250, 254
carp, 182
catfish, 104, 131, 151
cattle, 141, 182, 183, 184, 194–95, 273
cauliflower, 235, 237
celery, 141, 164–65, 182, 237
cheese, 46–47, 65, 89, 174, 182
cheesecake, 171
cherry, 59, 89, 151, 162–63, 168, 182, 223, 234, 235, 236, 237
cherry pie, 163; mock, 40
chess pie, 116
chestnut, 20, 59
chicken, 33, 92; fried, 99, 129–30, 162, 181
chicken corn soup, 78
chili con carne, 10, 195, 207*
chili peppers, 193, 206
Chinese cookery, 230–31
chinquapin, 151
chitterlings, 113–14

285